Treasures

Practice Book B

Macmillan
McGraw-Hill

B

The McGraw·Hill Companies

Mc Graw Hill Macmillan McGraw-Hill

Published by Macmillan/McGraw-Hill, of McGraw-Hill Education, a division of The McGraw-Hill Companies, Inc.,
Two Penn Plaza, New York, New York 10121.

Printed in the United States of America

4 5 6 7 8 9 10 024 09 08 07

Contents

Unit 2 • Outside My Door

Unit 3 • Let's Connect

Unit 4 • Our Earth

Unit 5 • I Can Do It!

Unit 6 • Let's Discover

© Macmillan/McGraw-Hill

Name _____

Read the question. Look at the picture. Write the answer.

1. Is this a mat or a man?

_____

- - - - - - - - - -

_____

2. Is this a cat or a can?

_____

- - - - - - - - - -

_____

3. Is this a rat or a rag?

_____

- - - - - - - - - -

_____

4. Is this a man or a map?

_____

- - - - - - - - - -

_____

5. Is this a pal or a pan?

_____

- - - - - - - - - -

_____

Write a sentence using some of the words above.

_____

- -

_____

 At Home: Ask your child to change one or two letters of the answers to make new words. Then have your child draw a picture of the words.

Pam and Sam • **Book 1.1/Unit 1**   ◇ 1

Name _____

Use the words in the box to complete the sentence.

up	down	not	jump

1. The house is _____ up.

2. The house is _____ .

3. The frog can _____ .

4. He can jump _____ .

 At Home: Have your child read aloud the sentences. Then write a story for one of the pictures.

Name _____

As you read <u>Pam and Sam</u>, fill in the Character Chart.

Pam Can	Sam Can

How does the Character Chart help you remember the beginning, middle, and end of <u>Pam and Sam</u>?

At Home: Have your child use the chart to retell the story.

Pam and Sam • Book 1.1/Unit 1   3

© Macmillan/McGraw-Hill

Name _____

Read the story.
Think about the cat and the girl.
Finish the story.

Pam is a girl.

She has a black cat.

The cat likes to jump.

The cat can jump up.

The cat can jump down.

_____

- -

The cat _____.

Draw a picture to illustrate your sentence.

 At Home: Have your child write another story about a pet, such as a dog or hamster. Ask: *What is the pet's name? What does the pet look like? What can the pet do?*

Name _____

Use the letters in the box to make words.
You can use each letter more than once.

| c | m | p | b | r | f |

1. _____ ans   2. _____ ats   3. _____ aps

4. _____ ans   5. _____ ats   6. _____ aps

Draw a picture of three of the words.

At Home: Look through magazines and catalogs for pictures of words with the short *a* sound. Have your child say and then write the word.

Pam and Sam • **Book 1.1/Unit 1** ⟨5⟩

As I read, I will pay attention to the punctuation.

	Everyone looked at the spotted Chameleon.
6	He did not speak.
10	Then something happened.
13	"Look at Chameleon!" said Yellow Lizard.
19	"Now he is yellow. He can hide in the
28	yellow sunlight."
30	"Look at Chameleon!" said White Lizard.
36	"Now he is white. He can hide in the white
46	flowers."
47	"Look at Chameleon!" said Green Lizard.
53	"Now he is green. He can hide in the
62	green grass."
64	"Look at Chameleon!" said Brown Lizard. 70

Comprehension Check

1. How is Chameleon different from the other lizards?

2. What do you think Brown Lizard will say?

	Words Read	–	Number of Errors	=	Words Correct Score
First Read		–		=	
Second Read		–		=	

6 Pam and Sam • Book 1.1/Unit 1

At Home: Help your child read the passage, paying attention to the goal at the top of the page.

© Macmillan/McGraw-Hill

Name _____

Look at the picture.

Write the things in this picture that could happen in real life.

_____

- -

_____

- -

_____

- -

_____

- -

_____

 At Home: Together with your child, look through magazines for interesting photographs. Ask your child to talk about the differences between photographs and drawings.

Pam and Sam • Book 1.1/Unit 1 7

Name _____

Look at the picture. Find as many short <u>a</u> words as you can. You get five points for each word.

1. _____

2. _____

3. _____

4. _____

5. _____

6. _____

Points

7. _____

8. _____

At Home: Have your child use a picture from a magazine or coloring book, or draw a picture in which he or she can find things that contain short *a*.

Name _____

**Read each question. Look at the picture.
Write the answer to the question.**

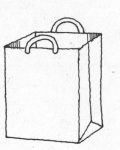

1. Is this a bag or a bat?

_____

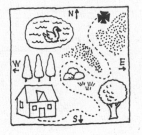

2. Is this a map or a man?

_____

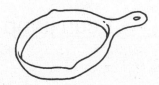

3. Is this a pan or a pat?

_____

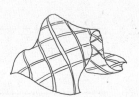

4. Is this a rag or a ran?

_____

**5. Write another word that has the
sound of short <u>a</u>.**

_____

© Macmillan/McGraw-Hill

At Home: Ask your child to say and draw a picture of some
other short *a* words.

I Can! Can You? • **Book 1.1/Unit 1**

9

Name _____

Complete each row.
Write a word from the box for each one.

Yes	over	it	too

1. Can you?   I can, _____ .

2. Can you?   I can jump _____ the hat.

3. Can you?   _____ , I can!

4. Can you?   I can do _____ !

© Macmillan/McGraw-Hill

At Home: Ask your child to make up a sentence for each word in the box.

Name _____

As you read <u>I Can! Can You?</u>, fill in the Sequence Chart.

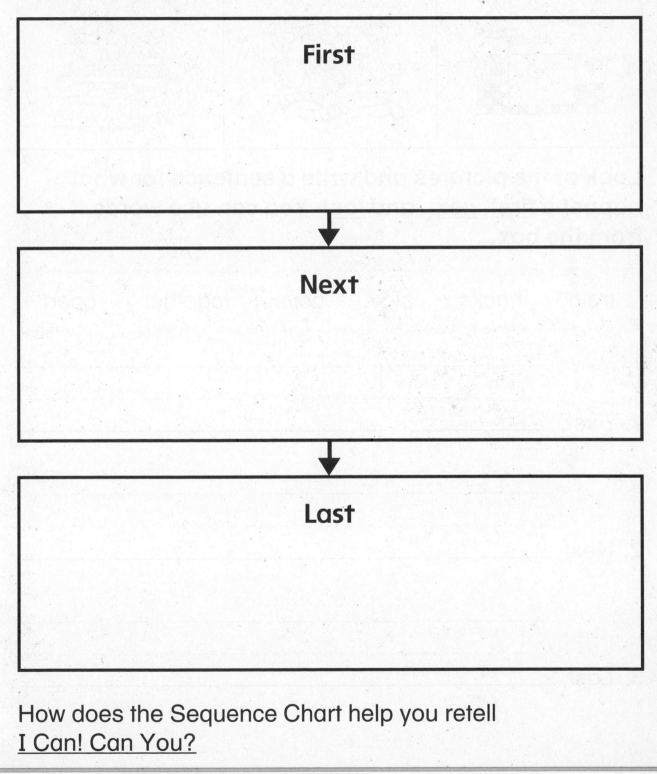

First

↓

Next

↓

Last

How does the Sequence Chart help you retell
<u>I Can! Can You?</u>

 At Home: Have your child use the chart to retell the story.

Look at the pictures and write a sentence for what happens <u>first</u>, <u>next</u>, and <u>last</u>. You can use words from the box.

| train | tracks | play | boys | together | open |

1. First, _____

2. Next, _____

3. Last, _____

At Home: Ask your child to tell you more about the details in each picture.

Name _____

Add -<u>s</u> to each action word.
Circle the words with the short <u>a</u> sound.

nap___ look___ tag___ pat___ play___ jump___

Use words from the box to write two sentences.
Draw pictures to illustrate your sentences.

_____

1. _____

2. _____

At Home: Have your child name action words for things
family members do at home: Mom _____, Dad _____,
The baby _____, The dog _____

I Can! Can You? • **Book 1.1/Unit 1**   13

© Macmillan/McGraw-Hill

As I read, I will pay attention to the punctuation.

	Many children like to ski.
5	At first, children ski down small hills. Then
13	they learn to go down longer trails. Someday,
21	they may even learn to jump over small
29	bumps in the snow.
33	There must be grown-ups near when
39	children ski.
41	Swimming is another sport children like to
48	do. Children learn to put their faces in
56	the water. It's fun to learn to stroke and kick.
66	Sometimes children learn to dive. 71

Comprehension Check

1. What things can children do when they learn to ski?

2. Do you have to be on a team if you want to ski or swim?

	Words Read	−	Number of Errors	=	Words Correct Score
First Read		−		=	
Second Read		−		=	

© Macmillan/McGraw-Hill

At Home: Help your child read the passage, paying attention to the goal at the top of the page.

Name _____

Look at the pictures. Read the labels.

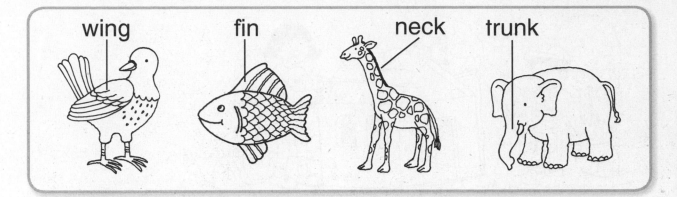

wing   fin   neck   trunk

Read each question. Draw a line to the answer.

1. Who has a fin?

2. Who has a wing?

3. Who has a trunk?

4. Who has a long neck?

© Macmillan/McGraw-Hill

At Home: Have your child draw and label a picture of a
favorite animal. Then have your child dictate a story about
the picture using the words in the labels.

Look at the picture. Write <u>yes</u> or <u>no</u> for each question.

             _____

1. Does Sam have a cap? _____

             _____

2. Does Pam have a bat? _____

             _____

3. Do Sam and Pam help? _____

             _____

4. Does Pat help? _____

             _____

5. Do the cats have hats? _____

© Macmillan/McGraw-Hill

At Home: Challenge your child to make one sentence with as many words on the page as he or she can manage.

Name _____

Look at the pictures. Complete each sentence with a word from the box.

dig	big	sit	pig	hit	did

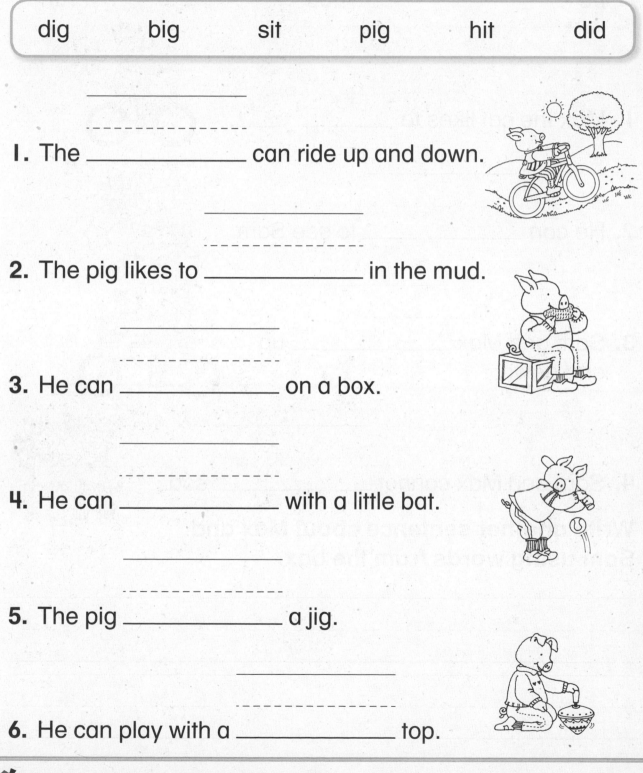

1. The _____ can ride up and down.

2. The pig likes to _____ in the mud.

3. He can _____ on a box.

4. He can _____ with a little bat.

5. The pig _____ a jig.

6. He can play with a _____ top.

At Home: Ask your child to use a word from the box to write another silly sentence about the pig. Have your child draw a picture to illustrate the sentence.

Name _____

Write a word from the box to complete each sentence.

| be | ride | run |

1. Max the cat likes to _____ .

2. He can _____ to see Sam.

3. Sam and Max _____ up and down.

4. Sam and Max cannot _____ sad.

Write another sentence about Max and Sam using words from the box.

_____

_____

_____

At Home: Have your child use words from the box to tell you a funny story about Sam and Max. Have your child draw a picture to illustrate the sentence.

© Macmillan/McGraw-Hill

As you read <u>How You Grew</u>, fill in the Sequence Chart.

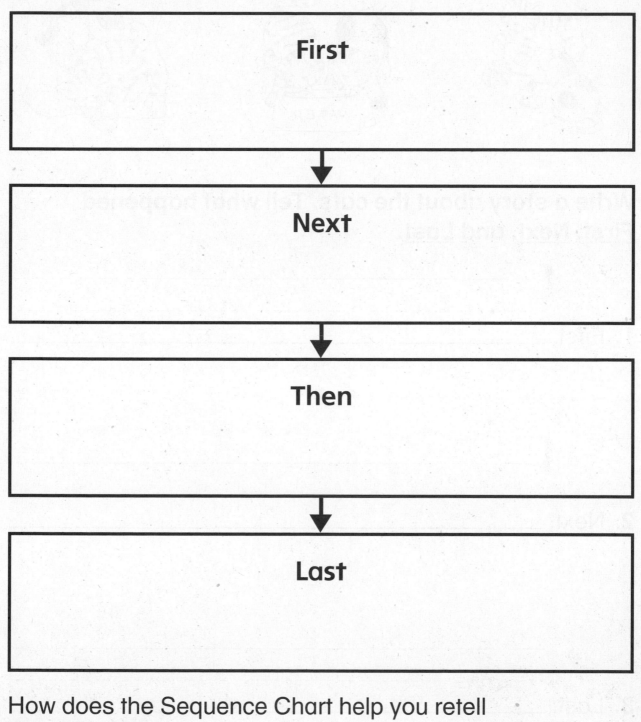

First

↓

Next

↓

Then

↓

Last

How does the Sequence Chart help you retell <u>How You Grew</u>?

At Home: Have your child use the chart to retell the story.

How You Grew • Book I.I/Unit I   ◆19◆

1   **2**   **3**

**Write a story about the cats. Tell what happened
First, Next, and Last.**

_____
- -

1. First, _____

_____
- -

2. Next, _____

_____
- -

3. Last, _____

At Home: Have your child make up a silly story about two animals. Draw three pictures that show what happens in the story in the correct time order. Talk about the pictures.

Name _____

ll	tt

Use letters from the box to finish the words in each sentence.

_____ _____

- - - - - - -   - - - - - - -

1. Bi_____ wi_____ play with his pup.

_____

- - - - - - - -

2. The pup wi_____ play with Bill.

_____

- - - - - - -

3. Bill and the pup run up the hi_____.

_____

- - - - - - -

4. Bill and Ma_____ play with the pup.

Write a sentence about the pup.

_____

- -

_____

- -

_____

At Home: Have your child look in books for words that end with the same two consonants.

As I read, I will pay attention to patterns in the story.

9	This girl likes to read. Her favorite books have
18	lots of pages. When she grows up, she might
27	want to be an author. An author writes books
35	for people to read. Some authors write books
	just for children.
38	The boy likes to help his dad cook. He likes
48	to watch people on TV cook.
54	When he grows up, he might want to be a
64	chef. A chef may cook for lots of people. 73

Comprehension Check

1. What does a chef do?

2. What would you like to be when you grow up?

	Words Read	–	Number of Errors	=	Words Correct Score
First Read		–		=	
Second Read		–		=	

At Home: Help your child read the passage, paying attention to the goal at the top of the page.

Name _____

Use the <u>Table of Contents</u> to answer the questions.

Contents

The Silly Cat   3

The Funny Pig   10

A Trip to the Park   21

A Trip to the Zoo   29

Cat and Pig
Are Friends   35

1. How many chapters are in this book? _____

2. On what page does "The Funny Pig" begin? _____

3. Which story begins on page 3? _____

4. On what page does a story about a park begin? _____

5. Is the chapter about a zoo near the front of the book or

the back of the book? _____

At Home: Have your child identify the cover, the title page, and the table of contents in a book.

Write a letter to Little Pig. Use words from the box.

pig	wig	dig	fit	did	wag	nap
fat	ran	back	sick	sack	bag	

_____

- - - - - - - - - - - - - - - -

Dear _____

_____

- -

_____

- -

_____

- -

_____

- -

_____

- -

_____

Your friend,

_____

- - - - - - - - - - - - - - - -

_____

At Home: Encourage your child to write a letter to a distant relative or to a friend who has moved. Help your child to address and mail the letter, or to send it in an e-mail.

Name _____

Read the words in the box. Circle the letters <u>br</u>, <u>cr</u>, <u>gr</u>, and <u>tr</u>. Write the picture names.

grass	crack	grin	trip
tracks	trap	bricks	crib

1. _____

2. _____

3. _____

4. _____

5. _____

6. _____

At Home: Ask your child to find pictures in books and magazines that begin with *br-*, *cr-*, *gr-*, and *tr-*.

Name _____

Read the words in the box.
Read the clue cards. Write the word.

come	good	on	that

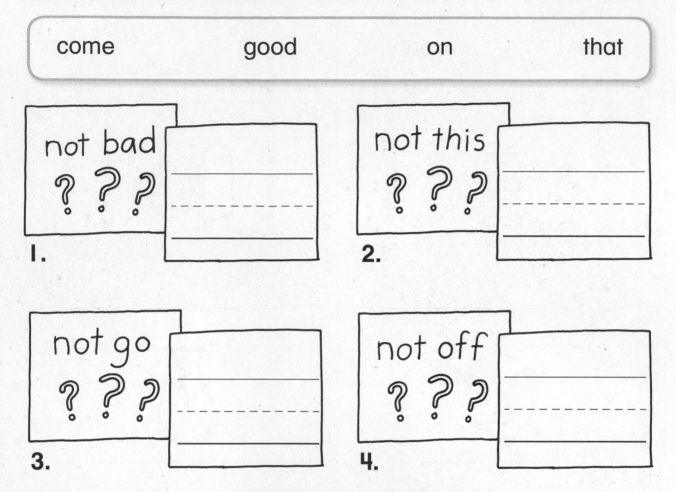

not bad
? ? ?

1.

not this
? ? ?

2.

not go
? ? ?

3.

not off
? ? ?

4.

5. Pick a word from the box. Write your own clue on one
card. Write the answer on the other.

?

At Home: Talk about other words that have opposite
meanings. Say a word and ask your child to name a word
that means the opposite. For example: up-down, day-night.

© Macmillan/McGraw-Hill

Name _____

As you read Pet Tricks, fill in the Setting Chart.

Setting	What the Characters Do There

How does the Setting Chart help you retell Pet Tricks?

At Home: Have your child use the chart to retell the story.

© Macmillan/McGraw-Hill

Name _____

Draw a cartoon story about characters that are two pets. You can make it funny, sad, or silly. Show the setting where the story happens.

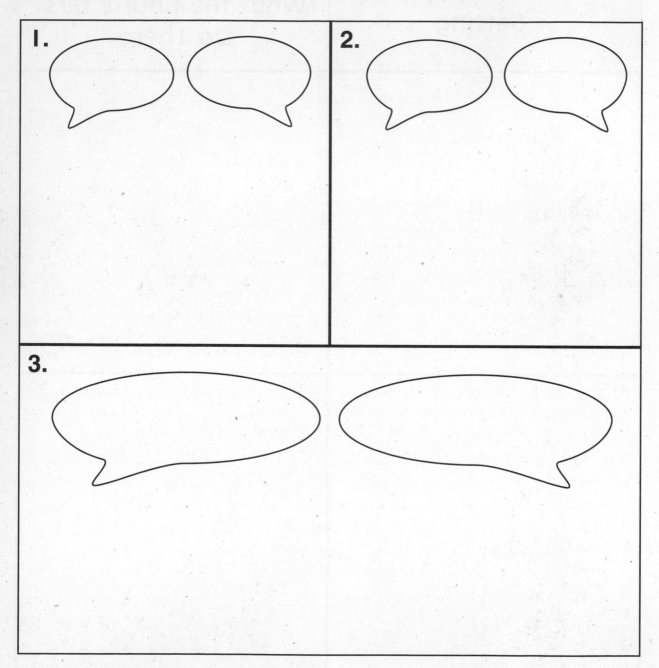

1.

2.

3.

Use the speech balloons to show what the characters say.

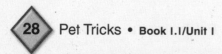
 At Home: Have your child tell you more about his or her story. Talk about the setting. How is it important? Discuss the characters. What are they like?

© Macmillan/McGraw-Hill

Name _____

Add 's to show someone has something.
Circle the picture it tells about.

_____
- - - - -
1. Brad____ pet is big.

_____
- - - - -
2. Fred____ grandpa has a cat.

_____
- - - - -
3. Grandma____ hat has dots.

_____
- - - - -
4. This is Mr. Trip____ truck.

Add 's to someone's name to finish the sentence.

_____
- - - - - - - - - - - - - - - -
5. This is _____ pet dog.

 At Home: Have your child use the possessive form to talk about things in your home, at school, or in your town.

Name _____

As I read, I will pay attention to vocabulary words.

	My name is Chris. This is my pet hamster Jazz.
10	He is brown with spots of white. He is little
20	and very cute.
23	This is his cage. It is where Jazz plays and sleeps.
34	He sleeps most of the day and is up most of the night.
47	There is a track in his cage. Jazz likes to race on it.
60	He goes up and down the track. 67

Comprehension Check

1. How does Jazz get his exercise?

2. When does Jazz sleep?

© Macmillan/McGraw-Hill

	Words Read	–	Number of Errors	=	Words Correct Score
First Read		–		=	
Second Read		–		=	

At Home: Help your child read the passage, paying attention to the goal at the top of the page.

A **list** is a series of things written in order.

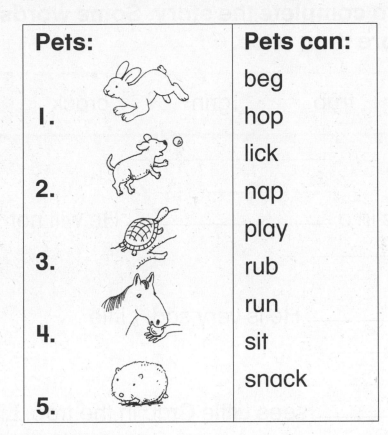

Pets:	Pets can:
1.	beg
2.	hop
	lick
3.	nap
	play
4.	rub
	run
5.	sit
	snack

Write a sentence about what one pet on the list likes to do.

_____

_____

_____

_____

_____

 At Home: If you have a pet, make a list with your child of the things you do to take care of it. If you do not have a pet, ask you child to make a list of desirable pets.

Read the story about two animals. Use the words in the box to complete the story. Some words may be used more than once.

| Frog | trap | grin | crack | Crab |

_____

Little Crab is in a _____. He will not

_____

_____. He is very sad. Little

_____

_____ sees Little Crab in the trap. Little Frog

_____

sees that Little _____ is sad. How can Little

_____

Frog help? She sees a _____ in the trap.

Look! Look! Look at that crack. Little Crab runs out of

_____

the _____. He is not sad now.

At Home: Encourage your child to act out the story. Perhaps members of the family would be willing to play different characters.

© Macmillan/McGraw-Hill

Name _____

Read each sentence. Complete each word by writing the missing letter blends. Write <u>nd</u>, <u>st</u>, <u>nt</u>, or <u>nk</u>.

1. Tom and I play in the sa___ ___.

2. I put on my pi___ ___ hat.

3. We look at an a___ ___ on a rock.

4. We cannot la___ ___ in the sun.

5. Tom and I sa___ ___ down on a mat.

 At Home: Ask your child to think of other words that end in *nd, st, nt,* or *nk* and use each word in a sentence.

© Macmillan/McGraw-Hill

Name _____

Look at the pictures. Use the words in the box to fill in the missing words in the story. Make up an ending for the story

very	help	use	Now

Pig and 🐿 are _____ sad. They need

_____

_____. What will they do? They will

_____

_____ the log. Squirrel will ride on top of pig.

_____   _____

_____ Pig and Squirrel will _____

.

At Home: Ask your child to tell you a funny story about two animals who help each other. Write it together. Draw a picture.

Name _____

As you read <u>Soccer</u>, fill in the Author's Purpose Chart.

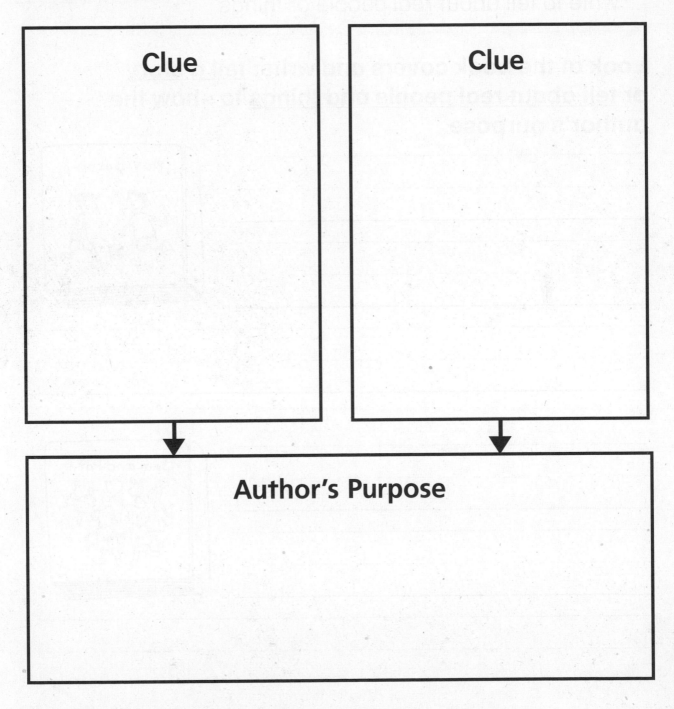

Clue	Clue

Author's Purpose

How does the Author's Purpose Chart help you understand the story <u>Soccer</u>?

At Home: Have your child use the chart to retell the story.

Name _____

Some authors write to tell a story. Some authors write to tell about real people or things.

Look at the book covers and write: <u>tell a story</u> or <u>tell about real people and things</u> to show the author's purpose.

_____

_____

_____

_____

Play Soccer!

_____

_____

_____

_____

Sam and Pat

 At Home: Ask your child to make up a story for Sam and Pat. Ask your child to tell how to play a game.

Name _____

Circle the words with a <u>final blend</u> in the box.

tent	went	pin	you	must	band
cat	nest	sand	rink	pink	
land	let	last	cast	best	

Finish the story about this silly picture. Use three of the final blend words in the story.

The elephants had a band. When they went to a new land—

_____

- -

_____

- -

_____

- -

_____

 At Home: Ask your child to use one of the words with a CVCC letter pattern in a sentence. Then have your child draw a picture.

Name _____

As I read, I will pay attention to vocabulary words.

	A family is one kind of team.
7	In a family, everyone can help with the meals.
16	Some members of the family can make a list and
26	shop. Others can do the cooking or take the dirty
36	dishes to the sink now.
41	Have you ever been on a meal team?
49	The people in this family team up to clean
58	their yard. They use rakes to gather the leaves
67	that have fallen. 70

Comprehension Check

1. What are the jobs on a meal team?

2. What is good about being on a team?

	Words Read	–	Number of Errors	=	Words Correct Score
First Read		–		=	
Second Read		–		=	

 At Home: Help your child read the passage, paying attention to the goal at the top of the page.

Name _____

Read the silly poem.
Add the rhyming words.
Draw a picture about
the poem.

Milly's Best Day!

1. Silly Milly has a car.

_____

- - - - - - - - - - - - -

Silly Milly can go _____

2. She rides and rides all day long.

_____

- - - - - - - - - - - - -

Milly likes to sing a _____

3. Milly sings to Tom the cat.

_____

- - - - - - - - - - - - -

When Milly sings, Tom can _____

4. Milly and Tom like to play.

_____

- - - - - - - - - - - - -

They will have a silly _____

 At Home: Have your child make up a silly rhyming poem
about two animal friends.

Name _____

Make words using the endings: -<u>nk</u>; -<u>nd</u>; -<u>st</u>; -<u>nt</u>. Put them in the correct column.

nd	st	nt	nk

Write a sentence using as many of the words as you can.

_____

_____

_____

At Home: Challenge your child to find words that end with one of the blends above. You might try to have him or her think of words related to sports.

© Macmillan/McGraw-Hill

Name _____

Look at the pictures. Read the sentences. Then write the numbers of the sentences in the boxes.

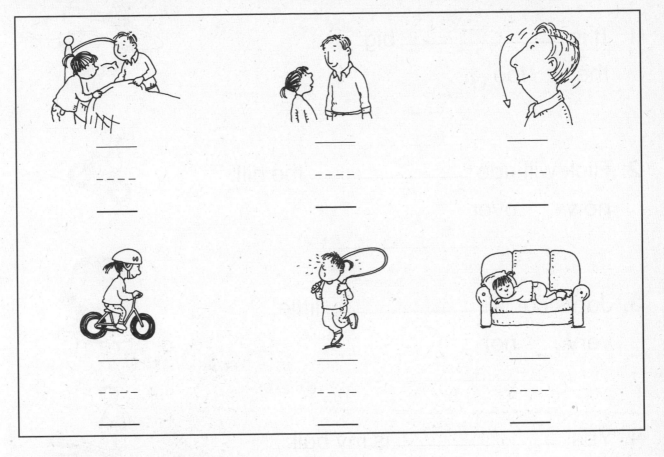

1. Dad said "yes."

2. Pat jumps up and down.

3. Pat helps Dad.

4. Pat can use a nap.

5. Pat rides.

6. Can Pat play now?

Name _____

Circle the correct word and write it on the line.

_____
- - - - - - - - - - - -

1. It is _____ big.

the   too

_____
- - - - - - - - - - - -

2. Rick will ride _____ the hill.

now   over

_____
- - - - - - - - - - - -

3. Jan's cat is _____ little.

very   not

_____
- - - - - - - - - - - -

4. Yes, _____ is my ball.

that   what

_____
- - - - - - - - - - - -

5. Will Stan _____ in the band?

back   be

_____
- - - - - - - - - - - -

6. Can you _____ over and play?

not   come

Read the question. Look at the picture. Write the answer.

1. Is this a pet or a pot?

_____

2. Is this a map or a mop?

_____

3. Is this a cot or a cat?

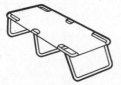

_____

4. Is this a leg or a log?

_____

5. Is this a sock or a sack?

_____

 At Home: Ask your child to write three more words that have the short *o* sound.

Animal Moms and Dads
Book 1.2/Unit 2

 43

Write words from the box to complete the poem.

Two	her	they	does	One

_____

_____ little bug,

Sits on _____ log.

What _____ she see?

_____ little frogs!

What do _____ say?

"Let's all play!"

Use words from the box to write two rhyming sentences.

_____

_____

_____

_____

At Home: Ask your child to make up a story about the game that the ladybug and frogs might play. Tell your child to use as many of the words from the box as possible.

Name _____

As you read <u>Animal Moms and Dads</u>, fill in the Main Idea and Details Web.

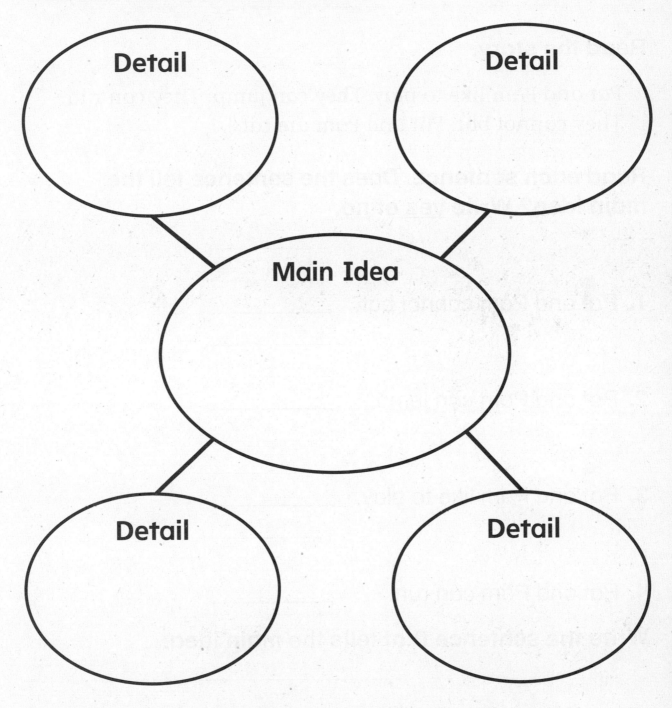

Detail

Detail

Main Idea

Detail

Detail

How does the Main Idea and Details Web help you
retell <u>Animal Moms and Dads</u>?

 At Home: Have your child use the web to retell the story.

Animal Moms and Dads
Book 1.2/Unit 2
45

Name _____

The **main idea** tells what the story is about.

Read the story.

Pat and Pam like to play. They can jump. They can run.
They cannot bat. Pat and Pam are cats!

Read each sentence. Does the sentence tell the main idea? Write <u>yes</u> or <u>no</u>.

1. Pat and Pam cannot bat. _____

2. Pat and Pam can jump. _____

3. Pat and Pam like to play. _____

4. Pat and Pam can run. _____

Write the sentence that tells the main idea.

5. _____

At Home: Show your child a picture from a magazine or a
book. Ask your child to tell the main idea of the picture.

Name _____

Add -ed to each word and complete the sentences.

wash	look	fish	rush
jump	wish	bark	pick

_____

1. Bob _____ at the clock.

2. He _____ out of bed.

3. He _____ his face and got dressed fast.

4. He _____ up his bag.

5. He _____ out the door.

Write a sentence to finish the story.

_____

6. _____

At Home: Have your child look in a magazine or a book for words that end in -ed and make a list of them.

Name _____

As I read, I will pay attention to patterns in the story.

	Baby elephants drink milk. They will drink
7	milk until they are three or four years old.
16	Baby elephants learn to use their trunks.
23	A trunk is like a long nose and lip.
32	An elephant uses its trunk to get food.
40	Baby elephants learn to eat a lot of grass.
48	Leaves and fruit are good, too.
54	A young elephant drinks at a waterhole.
62	The elephant uses its trunk to get the water. 70

Comprehension Check

1. What do baby elephants drink?

2. What do baby elephants eat?

	Words Read	–	Number of Errors	=	Words Correct Score
First Read		–		=	
Second Read		–		=	

At Home: Help your child read the passage, paying attention to the goal at the top of the page.

Name _____

Read the poem.

One little hog,
Was on a log.
She did not play,
She did not jog.

One little yak,
Sat on a crack.
He did not dance,
He did not quack.

1. Circle 3 words that rhyme in the first verse.

2. Box 3 words that rhyme in the second verse.

3. Underline 3 words that repeat in the first verse.

4. Underline 3 words that repeat in the second verse.

5. Make up another verse. Draw a picture.

_____

- - - - - - - - - - - - - - - - - - -

_____

- - - - - - - - - - - - - - - - - - -

_____

 At Home: Have your child write another verse for the poem.

Name _____

Finish each word ladder. Change only one letter at a time.

1. Go from hop to man.

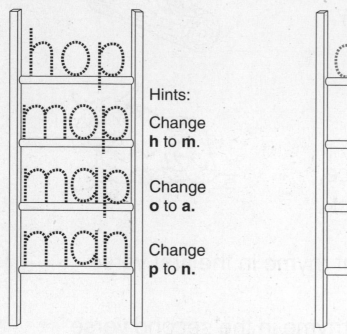

Hints:

Change **h** to **m**.

Change **o** to **a**.

Change **p** to **n**.

2. Go from dog to dad.

3. Go from bat to dig.

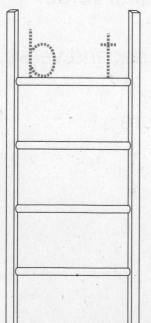

4. Go from hit to map.

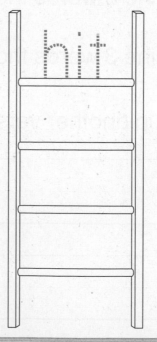

At Home: Have your child make up a word ladder with words that have the short *o*, short *a*, or short *i* sounds.

© Macmillan/McGraw-Hill

Circle the word that completes the sentence. Then write the word on the line.

1. She has a _____.

hat   ball   bell

2. Ted is in a _____.

fish   pen   band

3. The hen sits on a _____.

net   nest   pan

4. Jen likes her _____.

dress   vest   bat

5. Ben is in his _____.

tent   bed   ten

 At Home: Have your child make up sentences using two or more short *e* words.

Little Red Hen • Book 1.2/Unit 2   **51**

Name _____

Fill in the sentences with words from the box.
Draw a line from each sentence to who said it.

Who	some	of	No	eat

1. Look at my box _____ shells.

2. I like to _____ .

3. _____ said, I sit on my limb?

4. _____, thank you.

5. Can I have _____?

At Home: Let your child hunt in a magazine or newspaper for the words in the box.

© Macmillan/McGraw-Hill

Name _____

As you read <u>Little Red Hen</u>, fill in the Retelling Chart.

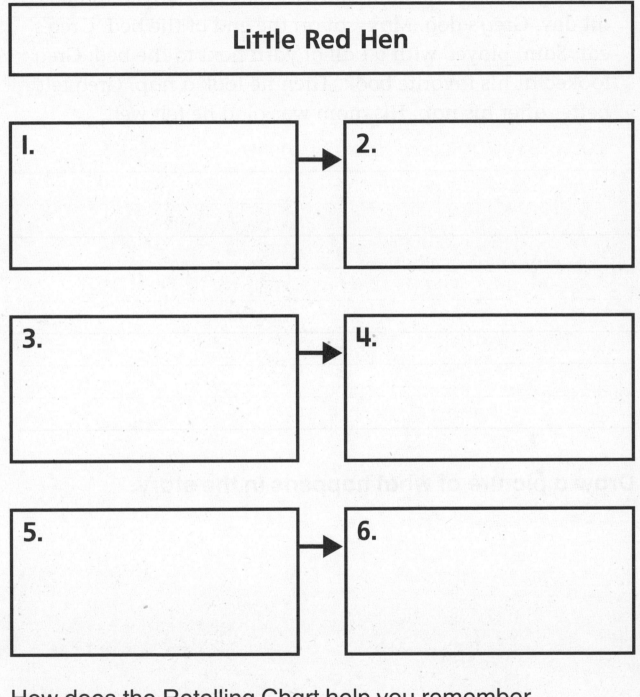

Little Red Hen

1.	2.
3.	4.
5.	6.

How does the Retelling Chart help you remember
<u>Little Red Hen</u>?

 At Home: Have your child use the chart to retell the story.

Read the story. Then write two or three sentences that tell important parts of the story.

Greg felt sick. He didn't go to school. He stayed in bed all day. Greg's dog, Max, sat on the end of the bed. Greg's cat, Sam, played with a ball of yarn next to the bed. Greg looked at his favorite book. Then he took a nap. Greg felt better after his nap. His mom was glad he felt well.

_____

- -

_____

- -

_____

- -

_____

Draw a picture of what happens in the story.

At Home: Ask your child what happened after school. Remind your child to tell you only the important parts of the day.

Name _____

Write a contraction to complete each sentence.

| can't | isn't | didn't | doesn't | aren't | don't |

1. Jen _____ at her desk.

2. Ben _____ have his backpack.

3. Len and Ted _____ here.

4. Ned _____ go to the play.

5. Greg _____ help us.

6. Fred and Jill _____ like to eat jam.

© Macmillan/McGraw-Hill

At Home: Have your child use contractions to tell you about his or her day at school. Help your child write the contractions he or she used.

Name _____

As I read, I will pay attention to questions.

How Do Trees Help People?

5	Trees give people food to eat. We get apples
14	and oranges from trees.
18	Do you know someone who eats bananas?
25	Trees give us this fruit, too.
31	We get wood from trees. Some trees are
39	planted and used for wood. Wood makes
46	good homes for people.
50	Some things in our homes are made of
58	wood, too. Some toys, tables, and chairs are
66	made of wood. 69

Comprehension Check

1. How do trees help people?

2. What fruits do you eat from trees?

	Words Read	−	Number of Errors	=	Words Correct Score
First Read		−		=	
Second Read		−		=	

 At Home: Help your child read the passage, paying attention to the goal at the top of the page.

**Pick three different animals from the diagram.
Add more labels to the diagram. Write a sentence
about where each one lives.**

_____

_____

_____

_____

_____

_____

_____

At Home: Have your child think of other animals and animal
homes to add to the diagram. Help your child add labels.

Little Red Hen • **Book 1.2/Unit 2**   57

Name _____

Complete the sentences with words from the box. Then find the words in the puzzle and circle them.

| pond | vest | mend | top | jet |

1. Meg plays with a _____.

2. Bob likes to fish in the _____.

3. Fred put on a _____.

4. Peg can _____ her dress.

5. Can I ride in the _____?

p	o	n	d	j
r	h	o	p	e
t	o	p	x	t
u	m	e	n	d
v	e	s	t	b

At Home: Have your child make up sentences using the short *e* and short *o* words.

Write sh or th to complete the words.
Then use your pencil to draw a picture for each
sentence.

1. A fi_____ is in my ba_____!

2. _____e _____ops for a di_____.

3. Be_____ said, "_____anks for the dress wi_____ red dots."

At Home: Have your child make up sentences for some of
the words that begin or end with *sh* and *th*.

A Prairie Dog Home • Book 1.2/Unit 2 ◇ **59**

Name _____

Write a word from the box in each sentence.

live	into	out	many

_____

- - - - - - - - - -

1. He jumped _____ the pool.

_____

- - - - - - - - - -

2. They _____ on a farm.

_____

- - - - - - - - - -

3. She likes to go _____ to eat.

_____

- - - - - - - - - -

4. I have _____ toy trucks.

Write two more sentences using the words in the box.

_____

- -

5. _____

_____

- -

6. _____

At Home: Have your child draw pictures for the sentences he or she wrote.

© Macmillan/McGraw-Hill

Name _____

As you read <u>A Prairie Dog Home</u>, fill in the Main Idea and Details Web.

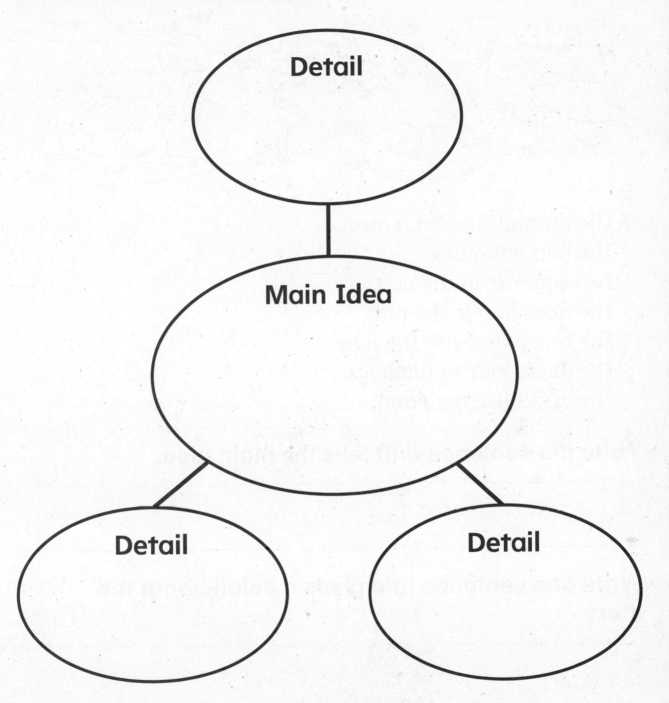

How does the Main Idea and Details Web help you better understand <u>A Prairie Dog Home</u>?

At Home: Have your child use the web to retell the story.

A Prairie Dog Home • **Book 1.2/Unit 2** 61

Name _____

Look at the pictures and read the story.

The animals live on a farm.
The hen has a nest.
Two eggs are in the nest.
The frogs hop to the nest.
The hen plays with the frogs.
The ducks look at the frogs.
The ducks like the pond.

Write the sentence that tells the main idea.

_____

- -

_____

Write one sentence that gives a detail about the story.

_____

- -

_____

At Home: Ask your child to describe additional details seen in the picture.

Name _____

Find these five words in the puzzle and circle them: <u>think</u>, <u>fish</u>, <u>rush</u>, <u>play</u>, and <u>go</u>.

p j r e t
l f u l g
a i s m o
y s h u p
t h i n k

Add <u>-ing</u> to three words from the puzzle. Use each word in a sentence.

1. _____

2. _____

3. _____

© Macmillan/McGraw-Hill

At Home: Have your child write another sentence using a word with *-ing*.

Name _____

As I read, I will pay attention to questions in the passage.

What Do Polar Bears Do?

5	A polar bear can live in this cold, cold
14	place. It has fur to keep it warm. The
23	fur keeps in the heat. A polar bear's
31	white coat helps it to blend into white
39	snow and ice.
42	There is so much ice in the Arctic. But,
51	polar bears do not slip and slide. Polar
59	bears have big, wide paws and strong
66	claws. 67

Comprehension Check

1. What is a polar bear's fur good for?

2. How do paws help a polar bear on ice?

	Words Read	−	Number of Errors	=	Words Correct Score
First Read		−		=	
Second Read		−		=	

© Macmillan/McGraw-Hill

 At Home: Help your child read the passage, paying attention to the goal at the top of the page.

Name _____

A **dictionary** gives the meaning of words.

cash   money

champ someone who wins

path   a track or trail for walking

think   to use your mind

Answer each riddle with a word from the dictionary.

1. You use this to buy things. _____

2. Walk on this when you take a hike. _____

3. You do this to answer a riddle. _____

4. The winner of a tennis match. _____

Write a sentence using a word from the dictionary.

_____

5. _____

At Home: With your child, look up these words in a dictionary.
Have your child read the meanings and example sentences.
Ask your child to create new sentences using these words.

A Prairie Dog Home • Book 1.2/Unit 2   65

© Macmillan/McGraw-Hill

Name _____

Write the word that completes each sentence.

| wish | shop | bath | path | ships | That | dress |

1. Fred likes _____ .

2. Beth has a red _____ .

3. They like to _____ .

4. I _____ I had that doll.

5. _____ is the one I want!

6. We can ride on this _____ .

7. Little Jim does not like to take a _____ .

At Home: Help your child write one or two sentences that use words with the digraphs *sh* and *th* and short vowel sounds *e* and *o*.

© Macmillan/McGraw-Hill

Name _____

Use words from the box to name the pictures.

| brush | drum | junk | cub | jug | truck |

1. _____

2. _____

3. _____

4. _____

5. _____

6. _____

 At Home: Ask your child to name a word that rhymes with a
word from the box.

Fill in the puzzle. Use the words in the box.

| make   want   under   put   show   three |

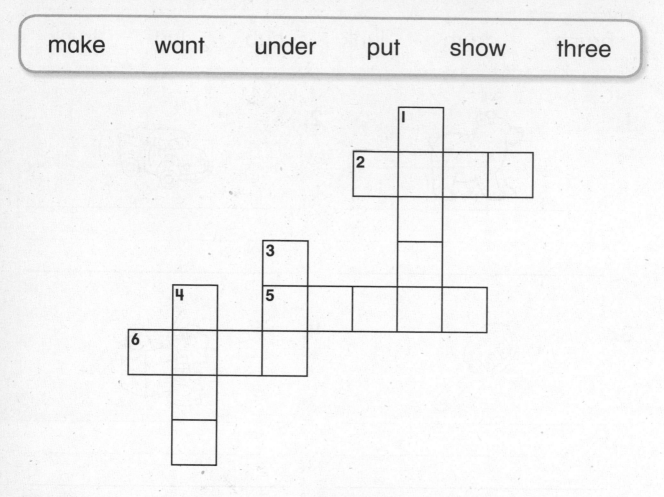

Down

1. Two plus one is ___.
3. He ___ the pen in the box.
4. I can ___ my bed.

Across

2. You can see a ___ on TV.
5. Your chin is ___ your lips.
6. You ___ something you wish you had.

 At Home: Make a new puzzle by scrambling the letters of each word in the box. Challenge your child to unscramble them and read the word.

© Macmillan/McGraw-Hill

Name _____

As you read <u>The Fun Kids' Band</u>, fill in the Retelling Chart.

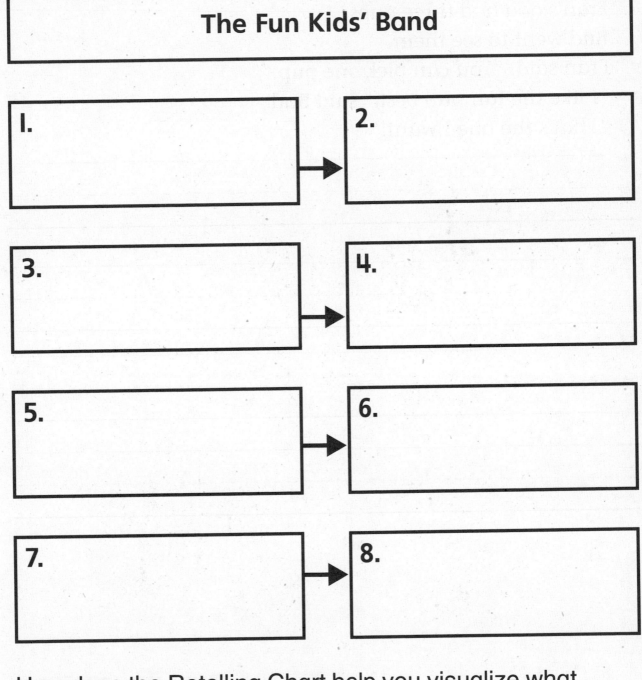

The Fun Kids' Band

1.

2.

3.

4.

5.

6.

7.

8.

How does the Retelling Chart help you visualize what happens in <u>The Fun Kids' Band</u>?

© Macmillan/McGraw-Hill

At Home: Have your child use the chart to retell the story.

The Fun Kids' Band • **Book 1.2/Unit 2**   69

Name _____

Read the story. Then retell the story.
Write the important parts.

Bud wanted a pet.
Fran's dog had three pups.
Bud went to see them.
Fran said, "You can pick one pup."
"I like the tan pup best," said Bud.
"That's the one I want!"

_____

- -

_____

- -

_____

_____

- -

_____

- -

_____

At Home: Read a story or watch a show with your child. Ask your child to retell the story. Remind your child to tell only the important parts.

Name _____

Write a **contraction** for the underlined words.

1. <u>She is</u> opening the trunk. _____

2. <u>What is</u> in the trunk? _____

3. <u>It is</u> just a dull drum. _____

4. <u>That is</u> rust on the top. _____

5. <u>Let us</u> rub it with a brush. _____

Write a sentence using one of the contractions.

6. _____

At Home: Have your child write a contraction for *he is* and use the contraction in a sentence.

The Fun Kids' Band • Book 1.2/Unit 2   71

Name _____

As I read, I will pay attention to the dialogue.

	Pam and Meg were twins. They looked just
8	the same.
10	Every Monday, Pam and Meg went to
17	skating class. Sometimes it was really hard to
25	tell them apart.
28	One day after class, Pam and Meg saw
36	a sign. The art center was going to put on
46	a show.
48	"Do you want to try out?" Pam asked Meg.
57	"I do, if you do," Meg said. 64

Comprehension Check

1. Why do Pam and Meg look the same?

2. Do Pam and Meg like to do things together?

	Words Read	−	Number of Errors	=	Words Correct Score
First Read		−		=	
Second Read		−		=	

At Home: Help your child read the passage, paying attention to the goal at the top of the page.

Name _____

Write directions. Use the words in the box.
Add some words of your own.

| bread | slices | other |

How to Make a Jam Sandwich

_____

- -

_____

- -

_____

- -

_____

- -

_____

At Home: Read a simple recipe. Talk about what to do first, next, and last. Then help your child read and follow the directions.

The Fun Kids' Band • **Book 1.2/Unit 2**

Name _____

Find the words in the puzzle.
Circle them.

band

truck

cub

nest

pig

brush

b	i	e	n	e	s	t	a
c	u	b	l	f	p	i	g
g	b	r	u	s	h	o	z
m	a	t	r	u	c	k	f
a	b	a	n	d	s	e	d

Write sentences using the words from the puzzle.

_____

- -

_____

- -

_____

- -

_____

- -

_____

At Home: Makek a word search puzzle with your child. Take turns choosing words that can be used.

Play with a partner.

Choose a word part from each column to make words. Take turns.

Write the words below.

cl   a   b
pl   e   p
bl   i   m
sl   o   nt
fl   u   d
gl   g
               ck

How many words did you make?

_____

You _____

Your partner _____

© Macmillan/McGraw-Hill

 At Home: Have your child use the words he or she made to write a silly story.

Use the words in the box to write about the pictures.

away	late	school	today	way	why

1.

_____

- -

_____

2.

_____

- -

_____

3.

_____

- -

_____

4.

_____

- -

_____

5.

_____

- -

_____

At Home: Ask your child to make up a story using the words in the box.

© Macmillan/McGraw-Hill

Name _____

As you read <u>On My Way to School</u>, fill in the Sequence Chart.

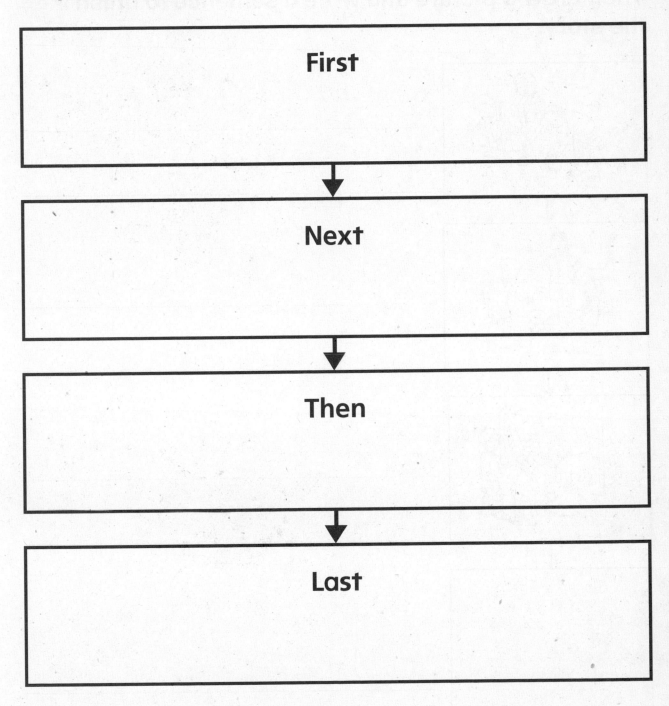

First

↓

Next

↓

Then

↓

Last

How does the Sequence Chart help you visualize what happens in <u>On My Way to School</u>?

 At Home: Have your child use the chart to retell the story.

Name _____

Write a sentence that tells about each picture.

Then draw a picture and write a sentence to finish the story.

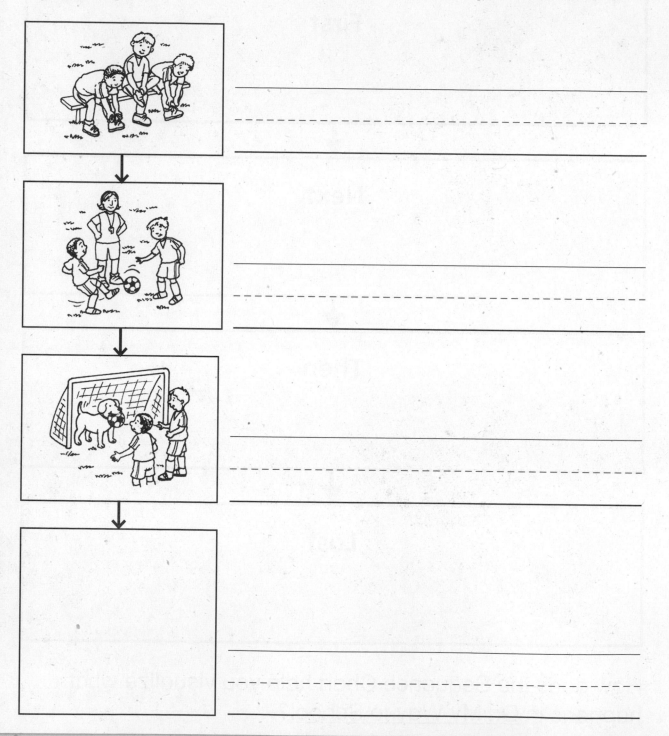

On My Way to School
Book 1.2/Unit 2

At Home: Have your child choose a picture from a book or magazine, and write a story about it. Remind your child to tell what happened first, next, and last in the story.

Name _____

Use the words in the box to complete the crossword puzzle.

| plum | flag | slip | glad | clap | slug |

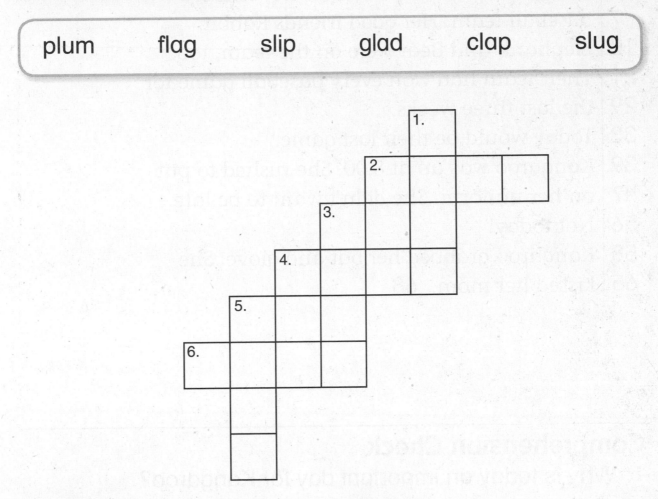

ACROSS

2. When you are happy, you are _____.

4. Another name for a snail is _____.

6. When the floor is wet, be careful not to _____.

DOWN

1. Our _____ is red, white, and blue.

3. _____ at the end of a show.

5. A _____ is a kind of fruit.

 At Home: With your child, look through magazines or catalogues for pictures of words that start with *l* blends. Cut them out and make a collage of the pictures.

On My Way to School
Book 1.2/Unit 2

 79

Name _____

As I read, I will pay attention to punctuation.

7	Kangaroo was the pitcher for her school's baseball team. Her good friends Rabbit,
13	Elephant, and Bear were on the team, too.
21	Their team had won every baseball game for
29	the last three weeks.
33	Today would be their last game.
39	Kangaroo was up at 8:00. She rushed to put
47	on her uniform. She didn't want to be late.
56	Not today!
58	Kangaroo grabbed her bat and glove. She
65	kissed her mom. 68

Comprehension Check

1. Why is today an important day for Kangaroo?

2. Is Kangaroo's baseball team a good team?

	Words Read	−	Number of Errors	=	Words Correct Score
First Read		−		=	
Second Read		−		=	

 At Home: Help your child read the passage, paying attention to the goal at the top of the page.

Name _____

Look at the signs. Draw a sign that means the opposite.

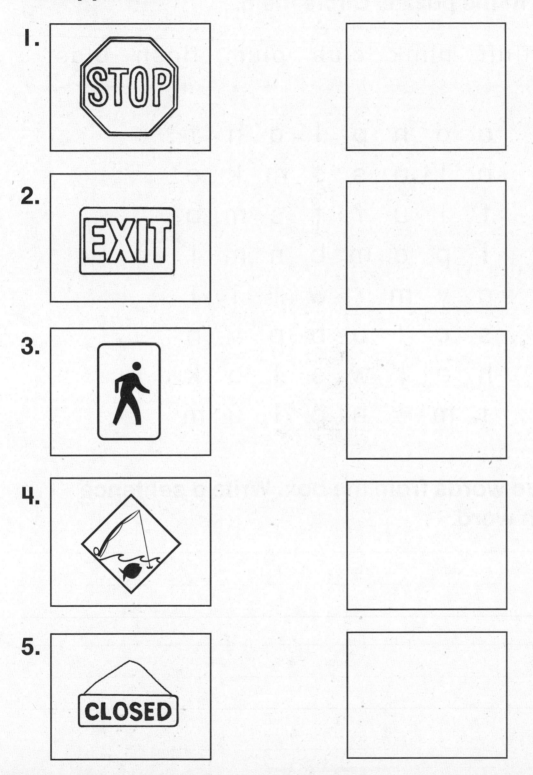

1.

2.

3.

4.

5.

 At Home: Take your child for a walk around your neighborhood. Have your child point out the signs. Ask your child what the words or pictures on the signs mean.

On My Way to School
Book 1.2/Unit 2
 81

Name _____

Read the words in the box.

Find them in the puzzle. Circle them.

| plant | fluff | blink | club | plum | flash | blast |

```
a  d  n  p  l  a  n  t
b  l  a  s  t  m  k  e
f  l  u  f  f  s  m  b
l  p  a  m  b  n  m  l
a  y  m  r  w  l  i  i
s  c  l  u  b  p  v  n
h  a  r  w  s  t  o  k
l  m  i  h  p  l  u  m
```

Choose two words from the box. Write a sentence using each word.

_____

_ _

_____

_____

_ _

_____

© Macmillan/McGraw-Hill

At Home: With your child, play this game: Write *sl, pl, bl, gl,* and *cl* on separate cards. Take turns picking cards and saying a word that begins with one of the *l* blends.

Look at the picture. Read the sentences. Then write the number of the matching sentence in the box.

 ☐

 ☐

 ☐

 ☐

 ☐

 ☐

1. Two pups get into the tub.

2. One pup gets out.

3. They want to eat.

4. Who is under the bed?

5. Some pups nap on the bed.

6. This pup runs away.

Name _____

Draw a line from the sentence to its picture.

1. Ted is on his way to school.

2. They are not late.

3. They live in a den.

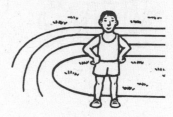

4. The dog has many pups.

5. They don't get wet.

6. He does run.

Name _____

Read the words. Find the words from the box in the puzzle. Circle them.

cake	rate	game	cane
ate	shade	shake	rake

```
r  a  t  e  b  f  d  m
a  i  a  s  h  a  k  e
k  g  t  h  w  l  u  q
e  a  p  s  h  a  d  e
k  m  x  c  c  l  n  v
e  e  g  o  a  y  d  a
n  s  o  b  k  a  t  e
c  a  n  e  e  r  j  z
```

What is the same about all the words in the puzzle?

_____

- -

_____

- -

_____

At Home: Have your child think of other words with the *a_e* pattern.

Name _____

Read the words in the box.

| hello | walk | pull | could | oh | all |

Draw a picture for each sentence.

1. I say hello to my friends.

2. Next, I walk to the park.

3. A dog and cat are hurt.
I say, "Oh, no!"

4. I pull all the pets in my wagon.

5. I ask the vet, "Could you help us?"

© Macmillan/McGraw-Hill

At Home: Write the words from the box on cards. Have your child make up a new story using some of these words.

Name _____

As you read <u>Kate's Game</u>, fill in the Predictions Chart.

What I Predict	What Happens

How does the Predictions Chart help you understand what happens in <u>Kate's Game</u>?

 At Home: Have your child use the chart to retell the story.

Name _____

Write a prediction about what will happen next.

1. A kid rides down a hill.

_____

- -

_____

2. A snake is under a tent.

_____

- -

_____

3. Two dogs see a cat.

_____

- -

_____

4. Mom makes a cake.

_____

- -

_____

5. Two kids are hot.

_____

- -

_____

© Macmillan/McGraw-Hill

At Home: Choose a book. Have your child write a prediction about what the book will be about. Have your child stop halfway through the book and revise the prediction based on what he or she has read.

Name _____

Circle the mistake in each sentence. Write the correct spelling on the line.

_____
- - - - - - - - - - - - - - -

1. I am takeing out the wagon. _____

_____
- - - - - - - - - - - - - - -

2. Dad is bakeing a cake. _____

_____
- - - - - - - - - - - - - - -

3. Liz gradeed the test. _____

_____
- - - - - - - - - - - - - - -

4. Tom bakeed a cake. _____

_____
- - - - - - - - - - - - - - -

5. I am tapeing the gift. _____

_____
- - - - - - - - - - - - - - -

6. It fadeed in the sun. _____

_____
- - - - - - - - - - - - - - -

7. Rakeing up trash is a big job. _____

_____
- - - - - - - - - - - - - - -

8. Gram tapeed the box shut. _____

At Home: Ask your child to tell a story using two of the words that he or she wrote.

As I read, I will pay attention to punctuation.

	A community is a place where people live
8	and work. People who work in a community
16	help in many ways. You may see some
24	workers all the time. And some workers you
32	may see just when you need them.
39	Oh, look! There is the crossing guard. A
47	crossing guard makes sure children walk
53	across the streets safely. She tells children
60	when it is safe to cross. The bus driver helps,
70	too. The bus driver pulls the door open and
79	waits for the children to get on. 86

Comprehension Check

1. How are community workers like friends?

2. How are crossing guards part of a community?

	Words Read	–	Number of Errors	=	Words Correct Score
First Read		–		=	
Second Read		–		=	

 At Home: Help your child read the passage, paying attention to the goal at the top of the page.

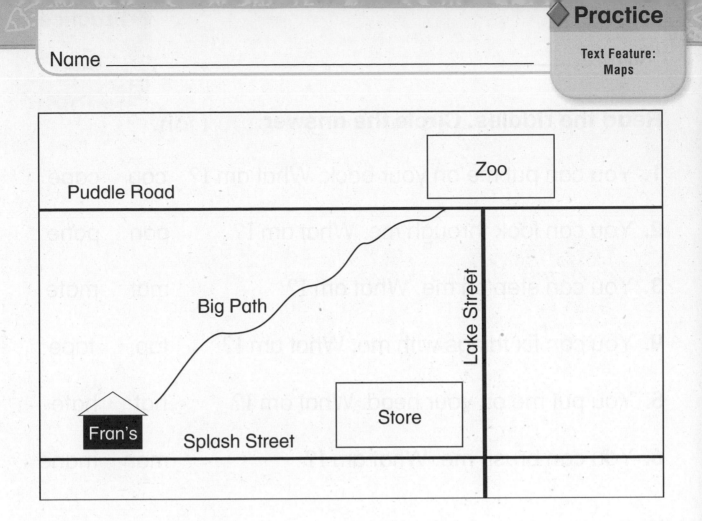

Look at the map.

1. Circle Fran's house.

2. Circle the zoo.

3. Fran is going to the zoo. Draw her path in red.

4. Fran's mom wants her to go to the store first. Draw a new path in blue.

5. Draw an ice cream shop on Puddle Road.

6. Draw a pond on Lake Street.

At Home: Have your child make a street map of a make-believe city. What would the streets be named? What places would there be to visit?

Name _____

Read the riddles. Circle the answer.

1. You can put me on your back. What am I? cap cape

2. You can look through me. What am I? pan pane

3. You can step on me. What am I? mat mate

4. You can fix things with me. What am I? tap tape

5. You put me on your head. What am I? hat hate

6. You can brush me. What am I? man mane

Write your own riddle. Use long <u>a</u> words.

_____

- -

_____

- -

_____

- -

_____

At Home: Write *ake* on a sheet of paper. How many words can your child make with these letters?

Name _____

Circle <u>yes</u> or <u>no</u> to answer the question. Then underline the words that have <u>s</u> blends.

1. Can you swing a scab?   yes   no

2. Can you spot a speck?   yes   no

3. Can you smell a snap?   yes   no

4. Can you spill a snack?   yes   no

5. Can you stop a swing?   yes   no

6. Can you spin a stamp?   yes   no

7. Make up your own silly question with <u>s</u> blend words.

_____

- -

_____

Draw a picture of one of the silly sentences.

At Home: Write *sw, sc, st, sn, sm,* and *sp* on small scraps of paper. Place them in a cup. Take turns choosing a blend and thinking of words that begin with that blend.

| When | water | boy | together |
| girl | people | care | |

Use words from the box to complete the sentences.

1. The _____ and _____
read a book.

2. It was about many _____.

3. They were taking _____ of Earth.

4. The people worked _____ to save _____.

5. _____ people work together, they can do
big things.

Kids Can Help • **Book 1.3/Unit 3**

At Home: Encourage your child to write a story using the
words in the box and draw a picture of something your family
can do to take care of Earth.

© Macmillan/McGraw-Hill

Name _____

As you read <u>Kids Can Help</u>, fill in the Compare and Contrast Chart.

Job	Kids in One Place	Kids in Another Place

How does the Compare and Contrast Chart help you better understand <u>Kids Can Help</u>?

At Home: Have your child use the chart to retell the story.

Name _____

Compare and contrast these pictures.

_____

- - - - - - - - - - - -

1. Is the number of kids the same? _____

_____

- - - - - - - - - - - -

2. Is the number of dogs the same? _____

_____

- - - - - - - - - - - -

3. Is the number of pets the same? _____

Tell other ways the pictures are alike and different.

_____

- -

_____

- -

_____

- -

_____

 At Home: Have your child compare and contrast his or her two favorite toys.

Name _____

Read the words in the box. Write all the one syllable words in the first column. Write all the two syllable words in the second column.

| swinging | tape | flag | baking | basket |
| taking | desk | sticking | step | smash |

1

2

_____   _____

_____   _____

_____   _____

_____   _____

_____   _____

_____   _____

_____   _____

_____   _____

_____   _____

_____   _____

Can you find other one-syllable and two-syllable words in your classroom?

At Home: Have your child look through a magazine to find one- and two- syllable words.

Kids Can Help • **Book 1.3/Unit 3**   97

Read the words and sentences below.

people

spill

spin

snake

water

Do not spill the water.

The girls and boys spin the tops.

The boys and girls sled together.

Draw a picture of one of the sentences.

At Home: Help your child read the words and sentences
above.

© Macmillan/McGraw-Hill

Name _____

Add a word to make these sentences more interesting or colorful.

_____

I. The _____ boat bobs on the water.

_____

2. The _____ cat purrs softly.

_____

3. The grass is tall and _____.

_____

4. The _____ smell fills the air.

_____

5. Clank! Clank! The train _____ down the track.

_____

6. The _____ bat dives in the night.

_____

6. The _____ frog jumped into the pond.

At Home: Have your child think of interesting words to describe an apple. Then have your child use those words to write a poem.

Kids Can Help • Book 1.3/Unit 3

© Macmillan/McGraw-Hill

Name _____

Circle the blends in these words.

snap   list   spit   disc

nest   scan   wisp   spin

Was the blend at the beginning or end of the word? Sort the words into two groups.

beginning   **end**

Use some of the words in a sentence.

At Home: Write the blends *sn, st,* and *sp* on cards. Then write the endings *op, it,* and *ud* on cards. How many words can your child make combining the blends with the endings?

Read each clue. Write <u>ch</u>, <u>wh</u>, or <u>tch</u> to complete the answer.

1. A dog can do this.

fe_____

2. You can eat this at school.

lun_____

3. Cats have these.

_____isker

4. You can sit on this.

ben_____

5. You can play this.

ca_____

6. You can ask this.

_____at

 At Home: Help your child think of more words with the *ch/tch* sound. Make up clues for the words.

Name _____

Write words from the box to complete the story.

Your	light	our	again	Would

_____

1. _____ you like to play a game?

2. We can play with the sun's _____.

3. Let's make shapes with

_____

_____ hands.

4. My shadow is small. _____ shadow is big!

Write an ending for the story. Use the word that is left.

_____

5. _____

At Home: Ask your child to tell you a new story about shadows using the vocabulary words.

© Macmillan/McGraw-Hill

Name _____

As you read <u>Short Shadows, Long Shadows</u>,
fill in the Main Idea and Details Web.

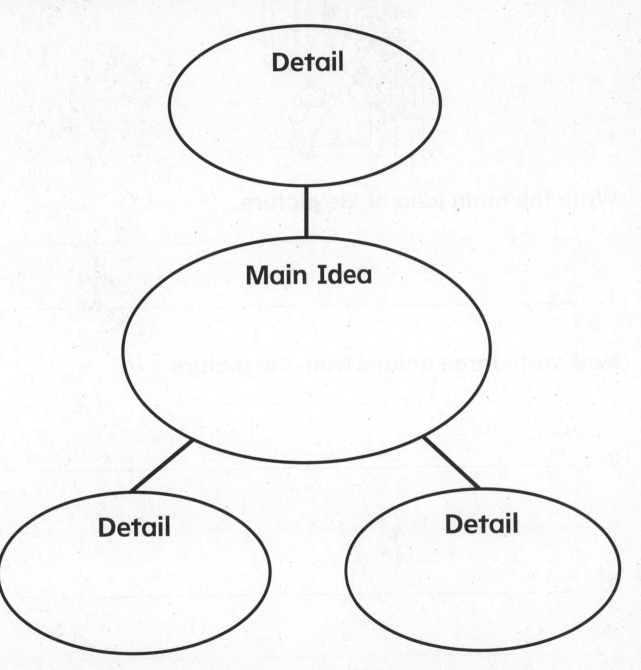

How does the Main Idea and Details Web help you
better understand the main idea of <u>Short Shadows,
Long Shadows</u>?

 At Home: Have your child use the chart to retell the story.

Short Shadows, Long Shadows
Book 1.3/Unit 3

103

© Macmillan/McGraw-Hill

Name _____

Look at the picture.

Write the main idea of the picture.

_____

- -

1. _____

Now write three details from the picture.

_____

- -

2. _____

_____

- -

3. _____

_____

- -

4. _____

 At Home: Invite your child to draw a picture of something
that happens at bedtime. Have your child talk about
the main idea of the picture.

Write ch, wh, or tch to complete each word. Then add -es to name more than one. Write the new word.

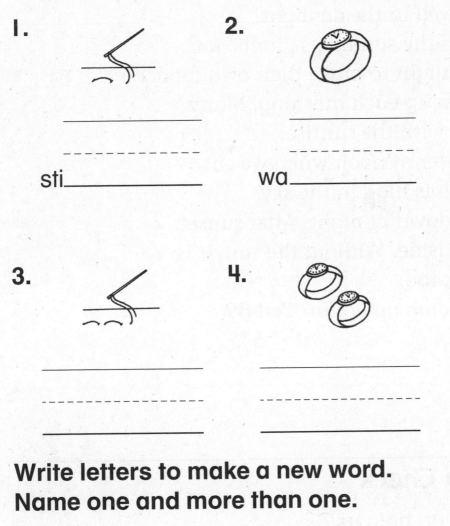

1.

_____

- - - - - - - - - - -

sti_____

2.

_____

- - - - - - - - - - -

wa_____

3.

_____

- - - - - - - - - - -

4.

_____

- - - - - - - - - - -

Write letters to make a new word. Name one and more than one.

_____

- - - - - - - - - -

5. _____ch

_____

- - - - - - - - - -

6. _____ches

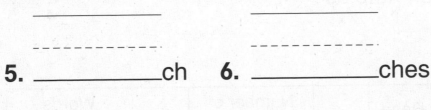

 At Home: Together, look in picture books for words that end with *-es*.

Short Shadows, Long Shadows
Book 1.3/Unit 3

 105

© Macmillan/McGraw-Hill

Name _____

As I read, I will pay attention to questions in the story.

	The light from the sun helps us see. We
9	can see very well in the daylight.
16	The light from the sun helps plants, too.
24	Plants use sunlight to make their own food.
32	The sun comes up each morning. Many
39	people get up with the sunrise.
45	The sun is hotter at noon when we eat
54	lunch. The sun is high in the sky.
62	The sun goes down at night. After sunset,
70	it gets dark outside. Without the sun, it is
79	colder outside, too.
82	Will the sun come up again? Yes! 89

Comprehension Check

1. How does the sun help us?

2. What is sunset?

	Words Read	−	Number of Errors	=	Words Correct Score
First Read		−		=	
Second Read		−		=	

Short Shadows, Long Shadows
Book 1.3/Unit 3

At Home: Help your child read the passage, paying attention to the goal at the top of the page.

© Macmillan/McGraw-Hill

Name _____

Make a cover for a magazine. Illustrate it.

What could you put in your magazine?

_____

_____

_____

_____

 At Home: Together, look at different magazines. Invite your child to look at the cover and predict what the magazine will be about.

Short Shadows, Long Shadows
Book 1.3/Unit 3
 107

Read each question. Circle the answer.
Then write the word.

1. Which one can hatch?

- -
_____

chick   check

2. Which one can you eat?

- -
_____

sandwich   bench

3. Which one lives in water?

- -
_____

whale   wham

4. Which one is part of a book?

- -
_____

chat   chapter

5. Which one holds water?

- -
_____

pitcher   catcher

At Home: Have your child write sentences for two of the uncircled words.

Name _____

Use the words from the box to answer the questions. Use as many long i words as you can.

| hike | hive | line | bite | bike |

1. How many boys and girls are playing together?

_____

- - - - - - - - - - - - - - - -

_____

2. What does Kim fly?

_____

- - - - - - - - - - - - - - - -

_____

Now write your own story about the picture.

_____

- -

_____

- -

_____

© Macmillan/McGraw-Hill

 At Home: With your child, make up a story about the picture.

Name _____

| call | How | more | funny | There | so |

Use the words in the box to complete the story.

_____

_____ are many nuts in Squirrel's house.

_____

_____ will Squirrel use the nuts?

_____

He will dig a hole_____ he can save some nuts.

_____

He will use _____ nuts to make things.

_____

He will _____ his friend to help.

_____

Squirrel reads a _____ book on his new bed.

 At Home: Ask your child to tell you a silly story about the squirrel. Write it out together.

Name _____

As you read <u>Smile, Mike!</u>, fill in the Predictions Chart.

What I Predict	What Happens

How does the Predictions Chart help you understand what happens in <u>Smile, Mike!</u>?

 At Home: Have your child use the chart to retell the story.

Read the story.

Jane was a very sad cat.
She did not have a nice hat.
Jean the dog can make nice hats.
Now Jane is calling Jean.

Write what happens next.

_____

- -

_____

- -

_____

- -

_____

- -

_____

© Macmillan/McGraw-Hill

 At Home: Have your child make up another adventure with the dog and cat. Then have him or her draw a picture to illustrate it.

Name _____

Add the ending to the word. Write the new word on the line. Then use the word in a funny sentence about the picture.

I. win + ing = _____

_____

_____

2. dip + ing = _____

_____

_____

3. flip + ing = _____

_____

_____

4. slip + ed = _____

_____

At Home: Have your child make up a funny story for one of the pictures. Then have him or her draw a picture to illustrate it.

As I read, I will pay attention to the dialogue.

	"So, did your tooth come out yet, Mike?"
8	Grandma asked.
10	"No, not yet," I said.
15	"I have something special for you,"
21	Grandma said gently.
24	She showed me a little silver box. There was a
34	whale sculpture perched on top.
39	"You can use this for your tooth when it
48	comes out," said Grandma. "I used it for my
57	first lost tooth."
60	"Thanks," I said. "It's terrific, but how can
68	I get my tooth to come out?"
75	"Just wiggle it and jiggle it some more,"
83	Grandma suggested. 85

Comprehension Check

1. What is on top of the box Grandma has?

2. How many teeth has the grandson lost?

	Words Read	–	Number of Errors	=	Words Correct Score
First Read		–		=	
Second Read		–		=	

© Macmillan/McGraw-Hill

 At Home: Help your child read the passage, paying attention to the goal at the top of the page.

Read the sentences about Mike's family and Kit's family. Then fill in the chart.

Mike has two brothers and three sisters.

Mike has four aunts and three cousins.

Kit has one brother and two sisters.

Kit has two aunts and five cousins.

Mike's Family	Kit's Family
_____	_____
_____ brothers	_____ brother
_____ sisters	_____ sisters
_____ cousins	_____ cousins
_____ aunts	_____ aunts

Answer the question.

Who has more brothers? _____

At Home: With your child, make a chart comparing the number of relatives in two different families.

Smile, Mike! • **Book 1.3/Unit 3** ◇ 115

© Macmillan/McGraw-Hill

Name _____

Read the words in the box. Find them in the puzzle. Circle them.

nine	slip	rim	time	smile	clip

```
b  d  n  i  n  e  p
l  c  l  i  p  o  t
r  p  o  r  i  m  l
w  s  l  i  p  d  e
t  b  s  m  i  l  e
c  h  t  i  m  e  o
```

Think of your own long i word. Use it in a sentence.

_____

- -

_____

- -

_____

Think of your own short i word. Use it in a sentence.

_____

- -

_____

_____

- -

© Macmillan/McGraw-Hill

At Home: Write the following letters on index cards: *ile, ide, ig, it.* Have your child pick a card and fill in letters to make a new word. Use some of the words in sentences.

Name _____

scr	str	spr	spl

Use the blends in the box to make words. You may use a blend more than once.

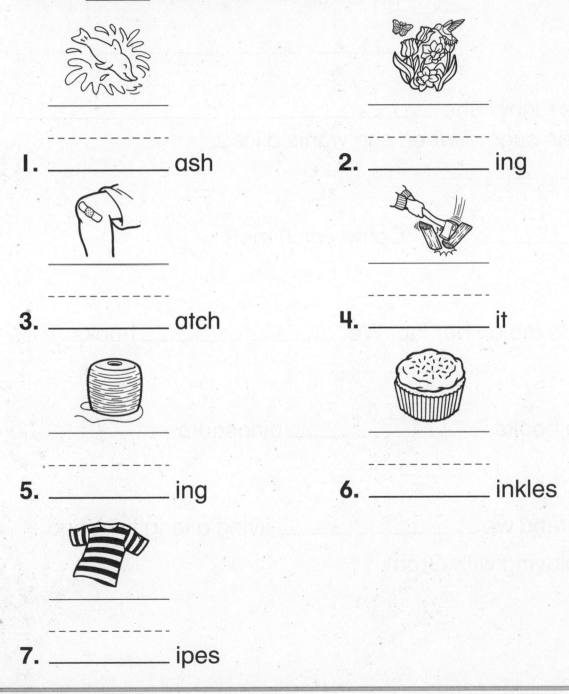

1. _____ ash

2. _____ ing

3. _____ atch

4. _____ it

5. _____ ing

6. _____ inkles

7. _____ ipes

At Home: Have your child make up a silly story about a cat named *Scruff*, using the words *strong*, *striped*, *string*, and *scratch*.

Gram and Me • Book 1.3/Unit 3

Name _____

Use words from the box to complete the story.

say	says	about	Give	read	were

My Gram

_____ _____

Gram is funny. She _____, "_____

me some sugar," when she wants a kiss.

_____

I _____, "Come catch me!"

_____

She puts me on her lap. We _____ books.

_____

We like books _____ dinosaurs.

_____

We pretend we _____ living a long time ago.

I love playing with Gram.

 At Home: Look at pictures of people in magazines. Help your child make up dialogue for the pictures using the words *say* and *says*. For example: The girl *says*, "I want pizza!"

© Macmillan/McGraw-Hill

As you read <u>Gram and Me</u>, fill in the Character and Setting Chart.

Setting	What the Characters Do There
1.	1.
2.	2.
3.	3.
4.	4.

How does the Character and Setting Chart help you retell <u>Gram and Me</u>?

 At Home: Have your child use the chart to retell the story.

Name _____

Draw a picture of a setting. Write a sentence to describe it.

_____

- -

_____

- -

_____

Write a sentence telling about two characters that could be found in this setting.

_____

- -

_____

Write a sentence telling what the characters might do in the setting.

_____

- -

_____

_____

- -

_____

At Home: Read a story with your child. Identify the setting and characters.

Name _____

Read each sentence. Circle the contractions.

1. We'll be home soon.

2. I've run a whole mile around the track!

3. I'll paint my face with stripes for my tiger mask.

4. They've been swimming in the pond.

5. I'm very tired today.

Write the contractions on the lines below. Write the two words that form the contraction.

He'll	He	+	will

6. _____ _____ + _____

7. _____ _____ + _____

8. _____ _____ + _____

9. _____ _____ + _____

10. _____ _____ + _____

At Home: Have your child write a sentence about what he or she will do in the future. The sentence should begin with the word *I'll*.

Gram and Me • **Book 1.3/Unit 3** 121

As I read, I will pay attention to the dialogue.

	Dad calls into my room and says, "Are you
9	up? It's time!"
12	"I'm up!" I say. I spring out of bed and race
23	to get dressed.
26	Dad is taking me on a trip today! He's
35	going to show me where he lived when he
44	was little. It will be just the two of us together.
55	"Don't forget your camera," Dad says.
61	"I didn't forget. I'm going to take lots of
70	pictures."
71	I can see a sprinkling of snow on the
80	ground. It's so cold I can see my breath. 89

Comprehension Check

1. What is Dad going to do on the trip?

2. Do you know where your parents lived when they were little?

	Words Read	−	Number of Errors	=	Words Correct Score
First Read		−		=	
Second Read		−		=	

 At Home: Help your child read the passage, paying attention to the goal at the top of the page.

Which of these activities would you like best? Put them in a list. You can add other activities you like to do. Number your list.

picking plums

playing chess

scratching a cat

reading

riding a bike

waving at boats

My Favorite Activities

_____

_____

_____

_____

_____

 At Home: Have your child make a list of things he or she does to get ready for school in the morning. Encourage your child to use numbers to help organize the list in order.

Name _____

Read each sentence. Circle <u>yes</u> if it is true. Circle <u>no</u> if it is false. Underline the words that have blends.

1. The sun is blue.   yes   no

2. A snake can say hello.   yes   no

3. You use a bat to spread butter on bread.
                                                              yes   no

4. This lane is very wide.   yes   no

5. A kid can use string at school.
                                                              yes   no

6. A sheep has three stripes.   yes   no

© Macmillan/McGraw-Hill

At Home: Have your child make up a tongue twister using several of these words: *strawberry, swallow, slurp, spill, snack, spoon, sweet.*

Name _____

Use words from the box to complete the sentences.

| walk   read   together   water   how   boys   about   give |

1. Jake can read _____ pets.

2. Mike dives in the _____ .

3. I will _____ my cat water.

4. _____ old are you?

5. I like to _____ about bugs.

6. Jake and Mike _____ to school.

7. The _____ likes to play.

8. They ride _____ all the time.

Name _____

| our | were | could | say | call | again |
| hello | light | more | people | pull | there |

Circle each word in the puzzle.

h e l l o r c a l l p
a g a i n g l i g h t
z m o r e q w e r e m
t h e r e c j p u l l
y p e o p l e x o u r
x s a y c t c o u l d

Pick three words from the box. Then write a sentence for each one.

_____

1. _____

2. _____

3. _____

© Macmillan/McGraw-Hill

Use the words from the box to complete the puzzle.

| joke | nose | close | home | globe | rose |

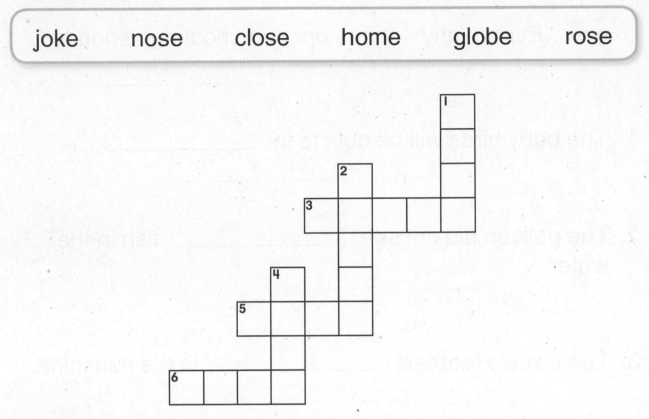

Across

3. This is a map shaped like a ball.

5. This is a red flower.

6. This is very funny.

Down

1. This is on your face.

2. This is another word for shut.

4. This is another name for house.

© Macmillan/McGraw-Hill

At Home: Ask your child to find five other long *o* words in a storybook. Together, create a crossword puzzle using the words your child found.

Pelican Was Hungry
Book 1.4/Unit 4
127

Name _____

Use words from the box to complete the sentences.

saw Every any soon opened floating sparkled

1. The baby birds will be able to fly _____.

2. The pelican did not see _____ fish in the water.

3. The swan's feathers _____ in the sunshine.

4. The robin looked and _____ a thick worm on the ground.

5. _____ day, the geese were _____ on the pond.

6. The baby birds _____ their beaks wide.

© Macmillan/McGraw-Hill

At Home: Ask your child to tell you about a day in the life of a bird. Then write a short paragraph together.

Name _____

As you read <u>Pelican Was Hungry</u>, fill in the Inference Chart.

Text Clues	What You Know	Inferences

How does the Inference Chart help you better understand <u>Pelican Was Hungry</u>?

At Home: Have your child use the chart to retell the story.

Read the story.

Ted and Pam walked to the pond.

The pond was filled with ice.

The white snow was piled up by the pond.

Ted and Pam saw no ducks.

They saw no frogs.

They saw no fish jumping up and down.

"Let's come back Sunday," they said.

Write **T** if the sentence is true.
Write **F** if the sentence is false.

_____ **1.** Ted and Pam went to the pond in the winter.

_____ **2.** The fish left the lake because it was too cold.

_____ **3.** The pond is close to Ted and Pam's home.

_____ **4.** Ted and Pam will go to another pond.

_____ **5.** Ted and Pam will see animals when it is warmer.

At Home: Ask your child to explain how he or she
determined which sentences are true and which sentences
are false.

As I read, I will pay attention to the punctuation.

7	Hummingbirds can do amazing things. They move
18	their wings so quickly that these little birds seem to float
28	in the air. Their beating wings make a humming sound.
36	Hummingbirds can fly in any direction--up, down,
45	forward, and backwards. They have long beaks to help
50	them get nectar from flowers.
59	Ostriches are amazing birds because of their size. They
71	are the biggest birds in the world. They can grow to be
74	nine feet tall.
84	Ostriches are also amazing because they do not fly like
	most birds do. 87

Comprehension Check

1. How do you think the hummingbird got its name?

2. Why are ostriches amazing?

	Words Read	–	Number of Errors	=	Words Correct Score
First Read		–		=	
Second Read		–		=	

 At Home: Help your child read the passage, paying attention to the goal at the top of the page.

Name _____

Some words have more than one meaning.

> **outside** I. the part of something that is out: My little brother colors **outside** of the lines. **2.** outdoors or not inside: It is cold **outside** on the deck.
>
> **notice** I. to pay attention to something: Mom, did you **notice** the barn owl? **2.** a printed message to make something known: There was a **notice** that said, "No running."

Choose the meaning of the <u>underlined</u> word that is used in the sentence. Write the number of the meaning on the line.

I. Maria and Pedro go <u>outside</u> _____
and wave to Papa.

2. Did anyone <u>notice</u> the barn owl? _____

3. Did that man see the <u>notice</u> _____
about no surfing?

4. The <u>outside</u> of the box is white. _____

At Home: Together, make up some silly sentences using the two meanings of the word *notice* and the two meanings of the word *outside*.

© Macmillan/McGraw-Hill

Name _____

Read the word. Look at each picture. Then write a sentence about the picture using the word.

1. biggest

_____

- -

_____

2. taller

_____

- -

_____

3. fastest

_____

- -

_____

4. softest

_____

- -

_____

5. smaller

_____

- -

_____

 At Home: Have your child write sentences using the
following words: *softer, nicest, longest.*

Name _____

Read the poem.
Circle the sentences that repeat.
Then add your own lines to the poem.

Who Will Win?

The pelican can see.
The pelican is diving.
Pelican is hungry! Pelican is hungry!

His wings are wide.
Can the fish hide?
Pelican is hungry! Pelican is hungry!

Look! A big splash!
The fish makes a dash.
Pelican is hungry! Pelican is hungry!

Will the pelican dine
on a fish so fine?
Pelican is hungry! Pelican is hungry!

_____

- -

_____

- -

_____

- -

Pelican is _____.

- -

Pelican is _____.

At Home: Together, look through children's poetry books for examples of repetition. Read the poems aloud, having your child chime in where words or sentences are repeated.

Name _____

Write one or two letters on the line to make a word. Then write a sentence using the word you made.

1. ___ oke _____

2. ___ ine _____

3. ___ ake _____

4. ___ one _____

5. ___ ane _____

6. ___ ipe _____

7. ___ ike _____

 At Home: Have your child illustrate one of the sentences..

Pelican Was Hungry
Book 1.4/Unit 4
135

Name _____

Read the words in the box. Circle each word in the puzzle.

mule	Luke	June	huge
tube	tune	use	cube

```
a   m   u   l   e   t
b   d   h   u   g   e
r   t   l   k   t   c
j   u   n   e   u   u
y   b   r   l   n   b
t   e   u   s   e   e
```

Choose two words from the box. Use each word in a sentence.

_____

- -

1. _____

_____

- -

2. _____

At Home: Have your child make up a silly sentence using two or more long *u* words from the box.

Name _____

Use words from the box to complete the story.

find	after	done	old
new	work	terrific	creation

My New Robot

_____

My old robot does not _____ anymore.

_____

I will make a _____ one. I will use the

_____   _____

_____ parts. I _____

the old robot in my toy chest. I work very hard

_____

_____ school. Now I am finally

_____

_____. I like my new

_____   _____

_____. It is _____ !

At Home: Ask your child to make up a story using three words from the box.

**As you read June Robot Cleans Up, fill in the
Conclusion Chart.**

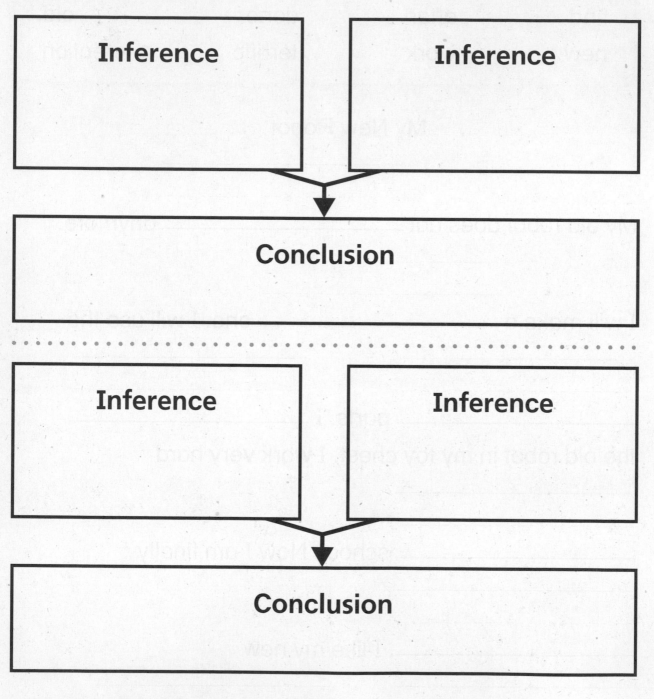

Inference

Inference

Conclusion

Inference

Inference

Conclusion

How does the Conclusion Chart help you better
understand June Robot Cleans Up?

© Macmillan/McGraw-Hill

Name _____

Read the riddles. Draw a conclusion from the clues. Circle the answer.

1. I have 4 legs and a tail.

   I like to play with a ball.

   Pat me and take me for walks.

   But I can't climb trees.

   What am I?

2. I live in the water.

   I do not have fins.

   I can move fast in the water.

   I do not move fast on land.

   I can hide in my shell.

   What am I?

3. **Create your own riddle.**

_____

- -

_____

- -

© Macmillan/McGraw-Hill

At Home: Ask your child to explain how he or she figured out
the answers to the riddles.

Name _____

As I read, I will pay attention to the punctuation.

	Look around! You can find things made of glass
9	everywhere you look. Glass is made into things
17	of all shapes, sizes, and colors.
23	Glass is used in many ways. Glass is strong enough
33	to be used for car windows. Glass can be used to hold
45	cold drinks or hot drinks. You can even cook in glass
56	pots. Buildings have windows, and sometimes doors,
63	made of strong glass. The glass lets in the light and lets
75	the people inside see out. The glass also keeps people
85	inside safe from the weather outside. 91

Comprehension Check

1. How is glass used?

2. Can you think of other items made of glass?

	Words Read	−	Number of Errors	=	Words Correct Score
First Read		−		=	
Second Read		−		=	

At Home: Help your child read the passage, paying attention to the goal at the top of the page.

Name _____

> **Context clues** are words in a sentence that help you figure out the meaning of a new word.

Use context clues to figure out the meaning of the underlined words. Write the letter of the meaning on the line.

Word Meanings:

A. a person who plays a musical instrument

B. to move very fast

C. the land along the edge of an ocean, a lake, or a river

D. most of the time

_____

- - - -

1. He had to <u>hurry</u> because he did not want to be late. _____

2. We walked along the <u>shore</u> digging our toes in the sand

____

- - - -

  and picking up seashells. ____

_____

- - - -

3. She <u>usually</u> takes the bus to school each morning. _____

____

- - - -

4. The <u>musician</u> played both the flute and the drums. _____

At Home: Together, think of some sentences that would help another person know the meaning of the words *scientist* and *laughter*.

June Robot Cleans Up
Book 1.4/Unit 4 141

Name _____

Play with a partner. Draw lines to make words. Take turns. You can use the same letter more than once. List the words.

b	a	k	e
c	a	s	e
m	i	t	e
n	i	n	e
h	o	b	e
r	o	l	e
t	u	p	e
f	u	g	e

How many words did you make?

_____

You _____

_____

Your partner _____

_____

\- - - - - - - - - - - - -

_____

\- - - - - - - - - - - - -

_____

\- - - - - - - - - - - - -

_____

\- - - - - - - - - - - - -

_____

\- - - - - - - - - - - - -

_____

\- - - - - - - - - - - - -

_____

\- - - - - - - - - - - - -

_____

\- - - - - - - - - - - - -

_____

\- - - - - - - - - - - - -

_____

 At Home: Have your child look for CVCe words in a book, newspaper, or magazine.

Name _____

A **floor plan** shows where things are in a room.

Use the floor plan to complete the sentences.

Recycling Center

Door

Desk

Plastic

Newsprint

Cans

Glass

1. There are _____ bins in the Recycling Center.

2. The bin for cans is next to the _____ bin.

3. The bin for _____ is the largest.

4. The smallest bin is for _____.

5. If you need help, go to the _____.

 At Home: Have your child draw a floor plan of your kitchen or living room. Help your child label his or her floor plan.

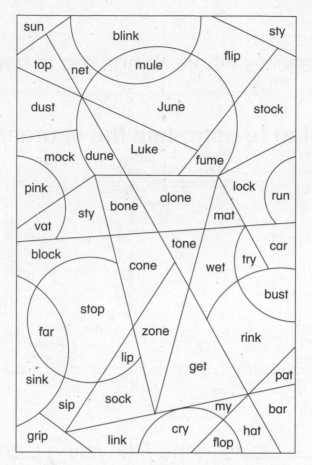

Words in puzzle: sun, blink, sty, top, net, mule, flip, dust, June, stock, mock, dune, Luke, fume, pink, lock, run, sty, bone, alone, mat, vat, tone, car, block, cone, wet, try, stop, zone, bust, far, lip, rink, sink, get, pat, sip, sock, my, bar, grip, link, cry, hat, flop, bone

Read the words in the puzzle. Color the spaces that have long <u>o</u> words tan. Color the spaces that have long <u>u</u> words pink.

What do you see?

_____

- -

_____

What kind is it?

_____

- -

_____

At Home: Next time you take a walk with your child, hunt for long *o* and long *u* words on store signs together.

Use words from the box to complete each question.

| trail | Jay | play | Spain | snail | train | tray |

1. Will it rain in _____ today?

2. Was it _____ who broke that _____?

3. Can Min _____ outside with us?

4. Is that a _____ on the gray pail?

5. We took a long ride on a _____.

6. We will take a walk along the _____.

 At Home: Together with your child, compose a verse with two rhyming long *a* words from the box.

Stormy Weather • **Book 1.4/Unit 4** ◇145◇

© Macmillan/McGraw-Hill

Name _____

Read the clues. Use words in the box to complete the puzzle.

predict	know	warm	cold
great	their	sound	extreme

Across

2. to be very sure

3. to tell what the weather will be

6. very good

7. when it is more hot than cold out

Down

1. you hear the _____ of the wind

4. very bad weather

5. belongs to others

Now fill in the last sentence.

8. We put on coats and hats when it is _____ out.

 At Home: Help your child to use some of the words in the box to retell a familiar story.

Name _____

As you read Stormy Weather, fill in the Compare and Contrast Chart.

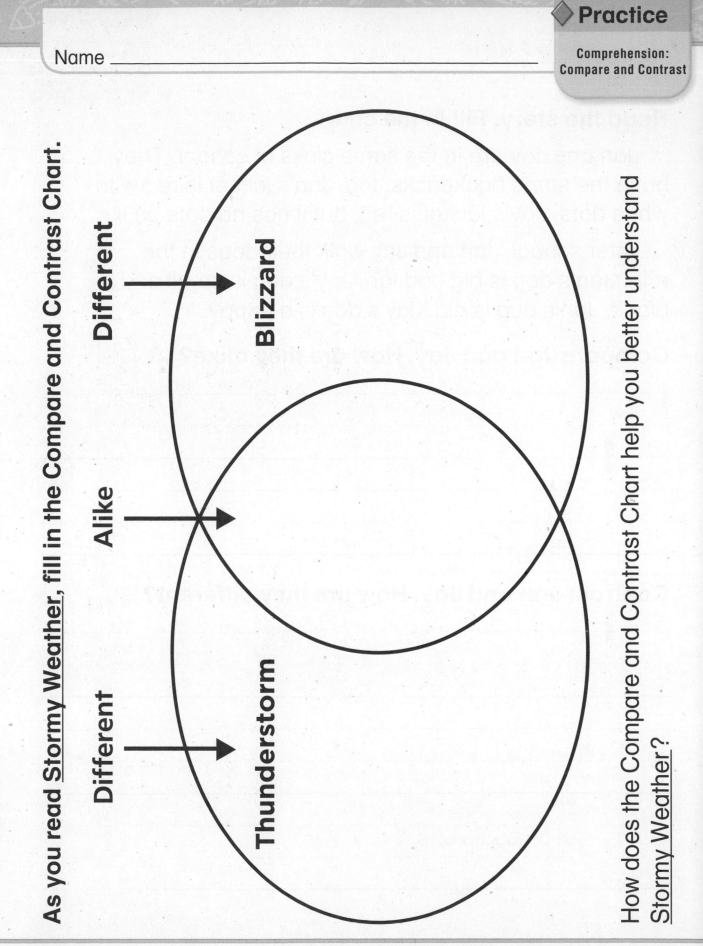

Different → Blizzard

Alike →

Different → Thunderstorm

How does the Compare and Contrast Chart help you better understand Stormy Weather?

At Home: Have your child use the chart to retell the story.

Read the story. Fill in the chart.

Jan and Jay are in the same class at school. They have the same backpacks, too. Jan's jacket is red with white dots. Jay's jacket is red, but it has no dots on it.

After school, Jan and Jay walk their dogs in the rain. Jan's dog is big and tan. Jay's dog is small and black. Jan's dog is old. Jay's dog is a puppy.

Compare Jan and Jay. How are they alike?

_____

_____

_____

_____

Contrast Jan and Jay. How are they different?

_____

_____

_____

_____

_____

_____

_____

 At Home: Ask your child to describe two pet animals he or she knows. Have your child tell how the animals are alike and how they are different.

© Macmillan/McGraw-Hill

Read the definitions below.

break 1. to divide into pieces: If you drop the glass, it will **break. 2.** a pause for rest or fun: She took a **break** from her homework.

store 1. a place where you buy things: You can buy food at a grocery **store. 2.** to put something away for later use: Mom will **store** my books in a box.

Choose the meaning of the bolded word that is used in the sentence. Write the number of the meaning on the line.

1. I will **store** the shells in a box. _____

2. She will go to the **store** to buy a backpack. _____

3. If you shake the box, the gift will **break**. _____

4. The class took a **break** and played a game. _____

At Home: Talk about other words that have mulitple meanings.

As I read, I will pay attention to the punctuation.

7	Sometimes snow falls gently, hardly making a sound. But sometimes snow falls hard with extremely
15	cold winds. Those snowstorms are called blizzards. In
23	a blizzard, there is a lot of snow and wind. The snow
35	lasts for a long time.
40	In places where it snows, people have to always be
48	ready for a blizzard. A blizzard can come at any time.
59	It is important to keep food and water, a radio, and a
70	flashlight with batteries in your home.
79	Skiers like when the weather reporter predicts snow.
87	They also listen to ski reports that let them know much
98	snow is on the mountain. 103

Comprehension Check

1. What happens during a blizzard?

2. Why do you need a radio and a flashlight during a blizzard?

	Words Read	–	Number of Errors	=	Words Correct Score
First Read		–		=	
Second Read		–		=	

At Home: Help your child read the passage, paying attention to the goal at the top of the page.

© Macmillan/McGraw-Hill

Jacob,	Mike	5 Overpass St.	555-5436
Jacob,	Paula	245 Main St.	555-7401
Jacob,	Tray	29 Sunset Ave.	555-4269
Jacob,	Willa	29 Sunset Ave.	555-4269
Jay,	Robert	29 Elm Ave.	555-7230
Jay,	Sam	17 Elm Ave.	555-9854

Use the telephone directory to answer the questions.

1. What is Paula Jacob's address and phone number?

_____

- -

_____

2. How do you know that Tray and Willa Jacob live together?

_____

- -

_____

Make a telephone directory entry for your family.

_____

- -

_____

_____

- -

_____

© Macmillan/McGraw-Hill

At Home: Have your child make a telephone directory entry
for a friend or relative.

Name _____

Use the words in the box to complete the compound words.

| in | day | pack | sun | up | thing | out | one | yard |

1. any**one** _____

   any_____

2. back_____

   back_____

3. _____side

   _____side

4. _____light

   _____light

Write two sentences using compound words from above.

5. _____

6. _____

At Home: Have your child look for other compound words in a book, newspaper, or magazine.

© Macmillan/McGraw-Hill

Name _____

Use a word in the box to answer each riddle.
One letter in the word is filled in for you.

play	sail	tunes	say
joke	nail	hole	flute

1. This makes you say "ha, ha!" __ __ k __

2. Do this to have fun. __ l __ __

3. You can do this on the water. __ __ __ l

4. You play this. __ __ __ t __

5. You can sing these. __ __ __ __ s

6. This is another word for talk. __ a __

 At Home: Have your child make up a riddle for a long *o*, long
u, or long *a* word.

Stormy Weather • **Book 1.4/Unit 4** ◆ 153

Name _____

Write <u>yes</u> or <u>no</u> next to each sentence.

1. Seals can walk. _____

2. Houses have teeth. _____

3. Eels can read. _____

4. Birds have beaks. _____

5. People have feet. _____

6. Dogs can speak English. _____

Use words from the box to write sentences that have a <u>yes</u> or <u>no</u> answer.

deep	bee	tree	seat	eat	we

7. _____

8. _____

 **At Home:** TK

Name _____

Read each sentence. Complete the sentence by writing the letter of the missing word on the lines below.

a. knew	**b.** kind	**c.** house	**d.** friends
e. By	**f.** far	**g.** curious	**h.** idea

1. Ben Franklin was a ___ boy. He asked about many things.

2. Ben's ___ knew he was special.

3. The people who ___ Ben liked his curiosity.

4. Ben lived in a ___ in Boston first and later in Pennsylvania.

5. He traveled ___ away and visited the colonies.

6. ___ the time he was older, he was an important person in American history.

7. Have you any ___ what a special person Ben was?

8. What ___ of invention is Ben best known for?

___ ___ ___ ___

1. ___   2. ___   3. ___   4. ___

5. ___   6. ___   7. ___   8. ___

At Home: Have your child write additional sentences using the words in the box and draw a picture to go with each one.

As you read <u>Meet Ben Franklin</u>, fill in the Inference Chart.

Text Clues	What You Know	Inferences

How does the Inference Chart help you better understand <u>Meet Ben Franklin</u>?

 At Home: Have your child use the chart to retell the story.

Name _____

Read the story. Use what you read and what you already know to answer the questions.

May looks at a tiger's teeth. "Oh no!" she says. "These have got to come out." Then she pulls two teeth. May makes sure the seals feel well. The seals are in a show. She tells a worker that one seal cannot be in the show today.

1. What is May's job?

_____

- -

_____

2. Where does May work?

_____

- -

_____

3. Why does May pull out the tiger's teeth?

_____

- -

_____

4. Why can't the seal be in the show today?

_____

- -

_____

At Home: Ask your child to explain how he or she figured out the answer to each question.

As I read, I will pay attention to the punctuation.

8	Bell and Watson knew that electricity could make sound travel over a wire. They wanted to send words
18	over a wire, too.
22	On March 10, 1876, an amazing thing happened. Bell
29	said, "Mr. Watson—come here—I want to see you."
39	Watson heard him. The sound of his voice came
48	through over the wires. They were the first words
57	spoken over an electric telephone. Bell's call to his
66	friend Mr. Watson was the first telephone message.
74	The telephone was a hit! Everyone wanted to have
83	one. 84

Comprehension Check

1. What makes sound travel over a wire?

2. What was the first telephone message?

	Words Read	–	Number of Errors	=	Words Correct Score
First Read		–		=	
Second Read		–		=	

At Home: Help your child read the passage, paying attention to the goal at the top of the page.

Name _____

Write the <u>base word</u> and the <u>ending</u>.

	base word	+	ending
1. flashed	flash		ed
2. flashing	_____		_____
3. pulled	_____		_____
4. pulling	_____		_____
5. filled	_____		_____
6. filling	_____		_____

Write a short story. Use some of the <u>-ing</u> or <u>-ed</u> words.

_____

_____

_____

At Home: Ask your child to make up a rhyme using one of the base words from above.

Name _____

Play with a partner. Draw lines to make words. Take turns. Write the words below.

b
d
f
h
l
m
r
s
t

ai

ea

ee

t
d
f
k
l
m
n
p
s

_____   _____

_____   _____

_____   _____

_____   _____

_____   _____

_____   _____

How many
words did
you make?

_____

You _____

_____

Your
partner _____

At Home: Have your child sort each word they made by the long *a* and long *e* sounds.

Bold print points out important words.

Read the story. Circle the words in <u>bold print</u>.

In Ben Franklin's time, books cost a lot of **money.**
So he and his friends started the first **lending library.**
These men, called the **Leather Apron Club,** would
put their money together and buy books. Then they
would lend the books to other people. Soon many
people got to read.

Answer the questions about the story.

1. When did books cost a lot of money?

_____

- -

_____

2. What is a lending library?

_____

- -

_____

- -

_____

3. How was the Leather Apron Club able to get the books?

_____

- -

_____

© Macmillan/McGraw-Hill

At Home: Help your child to make a picture dictionary using
the words in bold print. Have your child draw a picture of the
word, label it, and write the definition.

Name _____

Write more long <u>e</u> and short <u>e</u> words in the chart.

e	Long <u>e</u> ea	ee	Short <u>e</u> e
we	seal	feet	red

Write silly sentences using long <u>e</u> and short <u>e</u> words. The first one is done for you.

1. We met a seal with ten red feet.

_____

- - - - - - - - - - - - - - - - - - - -

2. _____

_____

- - - - - - - - - - - - - - - - - - - -

3. _____

_____

- - - - - - - - - - - - - - - - - - - -

4. _____

 At Home: Have your child write and illustrate another silly sentence that has long *e* and short *e* words.

© Macmillan/McGraw-Hill

Name _____

Read the riddles. Write the word from the box that answers each riddle.

penny	daddy	puppy	city

1. I am a big place.
Many people work in me.
What am I?

_____
- - - - - - - - - - - - - -
_____

2. I am cute and fuzzy.
I am a baby dog.
What am I?

_____
- - - - - - - - - - - - - -
_____

3. You can spend me.
You can save me in
a bank. What am I?

_____
- - - - - - - - - - - - - -
_____

4. I am a man.
I have a baby girl.
What am I?

_____
- - - - - - - - - - - - - -
_____

Make up riddle clues for the word <u>daisy.</u> Write them on the lines.

_____
- -
_____
_____
- -
_____

At Home: Have your child use the clue for *daisy* to ask you some riddles.

Name _____

Read the clues.

Write words from the box to finish the puzzle.

before	began	falls	glared
happen	haste	heard	told

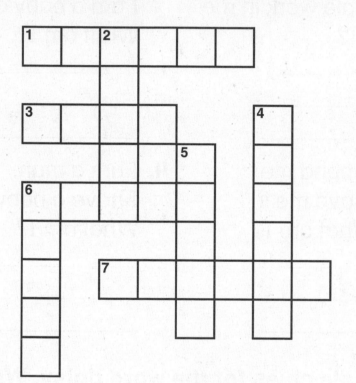

Across

1. not after

3. said

6. rush

7. looked mad

Down

2. drops

4. take place

5. started

6. used your ears

 At Home: Read a puzzle clue. Have your child say the word and use it in a sentence.

Name _____

As you read <u>Little Rabbit</u>, fill in the Beginning, Middle, and End Chart.

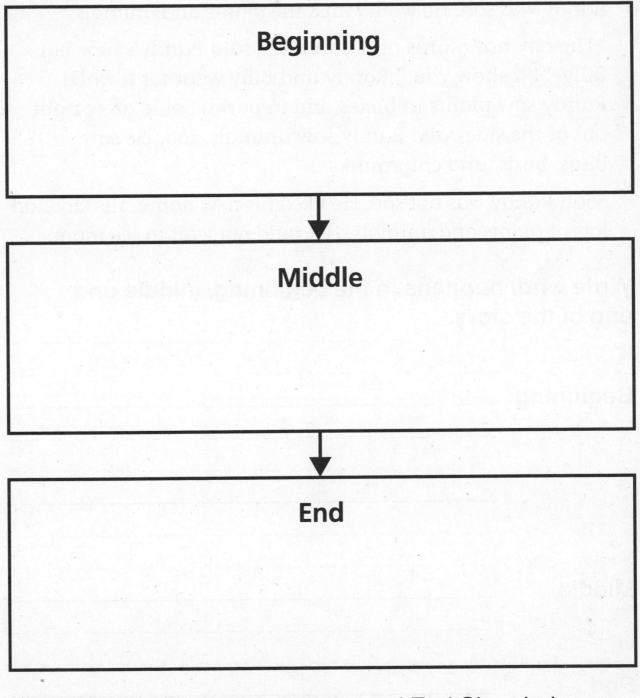

Beginning

Middle

End

How does the Beginning, Middle, and End Chart help you better understand <u>Little Rabbit</u>?

At Home: Have your child use the chart to retell the story.

Little Rabbit • **Book 1.4/Unit 4** 165

© Macmillan/McGraw-Hill

Name _____

Randy's New Home

Randy lived on a farm. Then he got a new home in a city.
Randy was sad. He would miss the plants and animals.

"The city has plants and animals," said Randy's new pal
Billy. "I'll show you." Randy and Billy went for a walk.
Randy saw plants in boxes and in parks. Some grew right
out of the sidewalk! Randy saw animals, too. He saw
bugs, birds, and chipmunks.

Soon Randy was not sad. He liked his new home. His city had
lots of plants and animals. He could not wait to see more.

Write what happens in the beginning, middle and end of the story.

Beginning _____

_____

Middle _____

_____

End _____

© Macmillan/McGraw-Hill

At Home: Ask your child to use a plot chart to plan a story.
Then have your child tell you the story.

Name _____

As I read, I will pay attention to patterns in the passage.

	Ant glared at the man who was starting
8	to build a trap with twigs. Ant knew that the
18	trap was for Dove.
22	Ant crept closer and closer. Ant knew that
30	Dove would fall right into the trap if Ant did
40	not do something. So Ant crawled onto the
48	bird catcher's leg and stung him with all his
57	might.
58	The sting made the bird catcher throw up
66	his arms. The twigs he was holding went
74	flying into the air. And the bird catcher ran
83	off. 84

Comprehension Check

1. How did Ant save Dove?

2. Do you always have to be big to help someone?

	Words Read	–	Number of Errors	=	Words Correct Score
First Read		–		=	
Second Read		–		=	

At Home: Help your child read the passage, paying attention to the goal at the top of the page.

Little Rabbit • Book 1.4/Unit 4 167

Name _____

> **Context clues** are words in a sentence that help you figure out the meaning of a new word.

Fill in the circle next to the word that completes the sentence correctly. Use the <u>underlined</u> context clues to figure out the missing word.

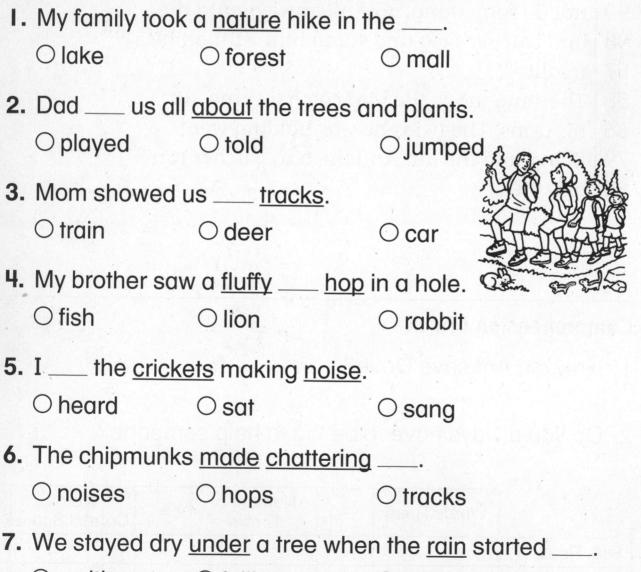

I. My family took a <u>nature</u> hike in the ___.
   ○ lake   ○ forest   ○ mall

2. Dad ___ us all <u>about</u> the trees and plants.
   ○ played   ○ told   ○ jumped

3. Mom showed us ___ <u>tracks</u>.
   ○ train   ○ deer   ○ car

4. My brother saw a <u>fluffy</u> ___ <u>hop</u> in a hole.
   ○ fish   ○ lion   ○ rabbit

5. I ___ the <u>crickets</u> making <u>noise</u>.
   ○ heard   ○ sat   ○ sang

6. The chipmunks <u>made</u> <u>chattering</u> ___.
   ○ noises   ○ hops   ○ tracks

7. We stayed dry <u>under</u> a tree when the <u>rain</u> started ___.
   ○ melting   ○ falling   ○ hiding

© Macmillan/McGraw-Hill

 At Home: Ask your child to use context clues to figure out unknown words on a cereal box or other food package in your kitchen.

Name _____

Add <u>es</u> to each word.
Write a sentence that has the new word.

1. hurry _____

_____

_____

2. study _____

_____

_____

3. city _____

_____

_____

4. buddy _____

_____

_____

At Home: Have your child draw a picture to illustrate one of
the sentences he or she wrote on the page.

Little Rabbit • **Book 1.4/Unit 4** ◇ **169**

© Macmillan/McGraw-Hill

Read the story starter.
Write the rest of the story. Use repetition.

Wake Up!

The animals were sleeping.
A man walked by.
The man woke a robin.
"Cheep! Cheep!" called the robin.

The robin woke a fox.
"Yip! Yip!" called the fox.

The fox woke a snake.
"Hiss! Hiss!" called the snake.

_____

- -

_____

- -

_____

© Macmillan/McGraw-Hill

At Home: Say a phrase like "Chug! Chug!" or "Knock! Knock!" Ask your child to tell a story in which the phrase is repeated.

Name _____

Play Tic-Tac-Toe with a partner. Take turns writing words.

You:

Write words that have the long <u>e</u> sound.

Your Partner:

Write three words that have the long <u>a</u> sound.

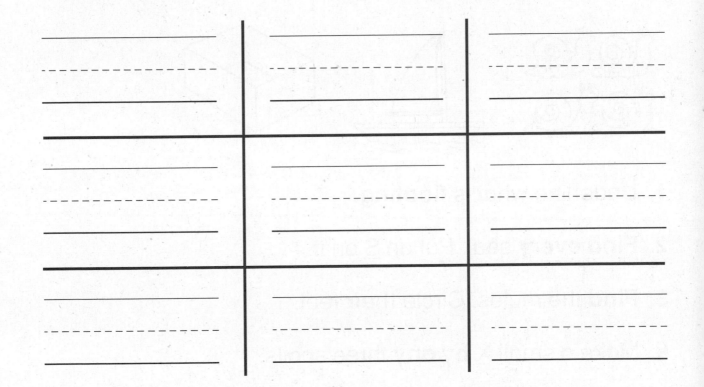

At Home: Play a few games of Long *e*/Long *a* Tic-Tac-Toe with your child.

Look at the pictures. Read the sentences and follow the directions.

1. Underline what is **floating.**

2. **Find every** seal. Put an <u>S</u> on it.

3. **Find** the mules. Circle **their** feet.

4. Make a small <u>X</u> **by any** three snails.

5. Put a <u>B</u> on what **told** a **great** tale.

6. Fill in the **sound every** bee makes.

7. Make a **new creation** in the big box.

Name _____

Read the sentences and questions. Then write a complete sentence to answer each.

I. What can **happen after** a lot of rain **falls**?

_____

- -

_____

2. Predict what you will do **soon.**

_____

- -

_____

3. Tell **any idea** you are **curious** about.

_____

- -

_____

4. What **terrific** place is **far** away?

_____

- -

_____

5. Tell something you have **done** in **haste.**

_____

- -

_____

Name _____

Write one or two words that rhyme with each word below and have the same <u>long o</u> spelling pattern.

1. go _____

2. moat _____

3. load _____

4. tow _____

5. coast _____

6. groan _____

7. goal _____

8. snow _____

At Home: Challenge your child to think of as many different rhymes for the word *low* as he or she can. Then sort the words by their long *o* pattern.

© Macmillan/McGraw-Hill

Name _____

Read each question. Write your answer on the line.

1. What is something you like to do with your **mother** or **father**?

_____

- -

_____

2. What is something you would like to **try**?

_____

- -

_____

3. What is something you **love**?

_____

- -

_____

4. What is something you are **supposed** to do?

_____

- -

_____

5. Are your mom and dad **firm** about bedtime?

_____

- -

_____

6. What do you **always** play with?

_____

- -

_____

At Home: Have your child write two more questions he or she could ask a friend.

**As you read <u>Olivia</u>, fill in the Fantasy and
Reality Chart.**

Reality	Fantasy
What Happens	**Why It Could Not Happen In Real Life**

© Macmillan/McGraw-Hill

How does the Fantasy and Reality Chart help you
better understand <u>Olivia</u>?

 At Home: Have your child use the chart to retell the story.

Name _____

Circle yes or no to answer each question.

1. Could a dog put on a dress?   yes   no

2. Could a pig build a house?   yes   no

3. Could a cat find a rat?   yes   no

4. Could a frog be a king?   yes   no

5. Could a duck swim in a pond?   yes   no

6. Could a lamb go to school?   yes   no

7. Could a lion have wings?   yes   no

8. Could a spider make a web?   yes   no

Make up your own <u>fantasy</u> questions.

9. _____

10. _____

Make up you own <u>reality</u> questions.

11. _____

12. _____

At Home: Have your child draw a picture of one of the fantasy questions. Talk about what makes it fantasy. Ask how he or she could change it to reality.

Name _____

As I read, I will pay attention to pauses for punctuation.

	"It's too hot in here," Dave called from his bedroom.
10	His mother and father came in. As always, his mother
20	suggested trying to read for a while. Then his father
30	handed him a new book.
35	"Try this book about snow," said his father. "It might
45	help you feel cool."
49	"Thanks. Good night," said Dave.
54	Dave skimmed through the book. He started reading
62	about snowstorms and places covered with snow. The
70	pages that really caught his attention showed snow
78	sculptures. Dave couldn't believe that so many things
86	could be made of snow. Soon Dave started to feel
96	very sleepy.
98	Then suddenly, Dave felt very cold. It was the middle
108	of summer but he found himself standing in the middle
118	of a maze made of snow. 124

Comprehension Check

1. How does Dave cool down?

2. Where does Dave dream that he is?

	Words Read	−	Number of Errors	=	Words Correct Score
First Read		−		=	
Second Read		−		=	

At Home: Help your child read the passage, paying attention to the goal at the top of the page.

Read the dictionary entries

build to make: She likes to **build** things with blocks.

journey a trip: We went on a **journey** to a state park.

moat a ditch filled with water that surrounds a castle:
A **moat** was used to protect a castle.

shore the land along an ocean, lake, or river: She
took a long walk on the **shore**.

Use words from the box to complete the sentences.

_____

Each summer I take a trip to the _____.

_____

Grandpa likes to read. I like to _____ sand

_____

castles. I always build a _____ around the

_____

sand castle. Each summer I enjoy my _____
to the shore.

At Home: As you read together, find three words your child
doesn't know. Work together to find the meanings of these
words in the dictionary.

Name _____

Add each ending to the words.

| y | -ed | -ing |

1. snow _____ _____ _____

2. toast _____ _____ _____

3. wax _____ _____ _____

Write two sentences using the words with the y ending.

_____

_____

_____

 At Home: Challenge your child to make up a story using two of the words above.

Add captions to go with each picture. You can use words from the box to help you.

circus	elephant	clown	horse

1.  _____

_____

2. _____

_____

3. 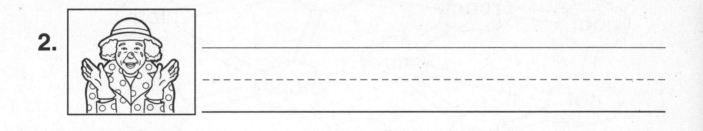 _____

_____

4. 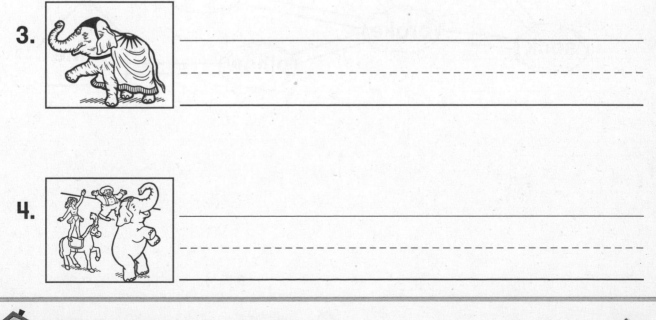 _____

_____

At Home: Help your child cut out magazine pictures.
Have him or her child write a caption to go with each
of the photographs.

Olivia • Book 1.5/Unit 5 181

© Macmillan/McGraw-Hill

Name _____

There are long o and short o words on the rocks. Help Olivia get Home by connecting the rocks with long o words.

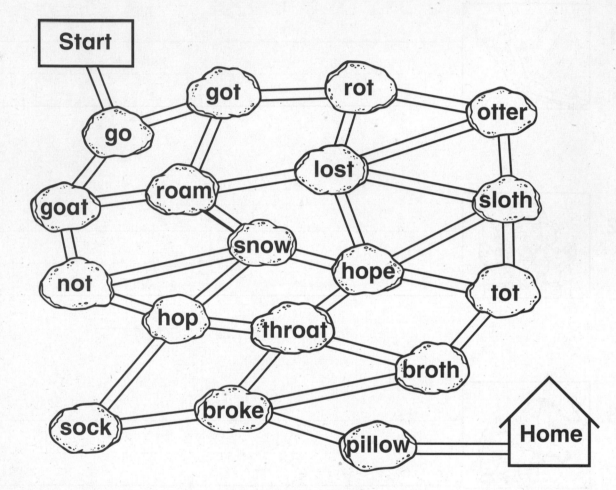

 At Home: Ask your child to create a maze using some song o words.

Name _____

Read the story sentences below. Fill in the blanks with words from the box.

| might | fly | mind | high | wild | try |

Sam is moving to a bright new home.

_____

It is very _____ in the tallest tree in

_____

the meadow. Sam can _____ to

push his things up to his new home.

_____

That _____ take Sam a very long time.

_____

Perhaps his friend Max can _____

Sam's things to his tree house?

_____

Max doesn't _____ helping his friend

_____

today. What a _____ ride for Sam!

At Home: Have your child make up another story about the animals in the picture. Encourage your child to use words from the box or other words with a long *i* spelled *i*, *igh*, or *y*.

The Kite • **Book 1.5/Unit 5**   183

Name _____

| head | never | should | ball |
| shout | laughter | meadow | perhaps |

Write a sentence for each picture. Use one or more of the words from the box in each sentence.

1. _____

2. _____

3. _____

4. _____

5. _____

© Macmillan/McGraw-Hill

 At Home: Have your child make up a story using some of the words in the box. Draw a picture of the story events.

As you read <u>The Kite</u>, fill in the Problem and Solution Chart.

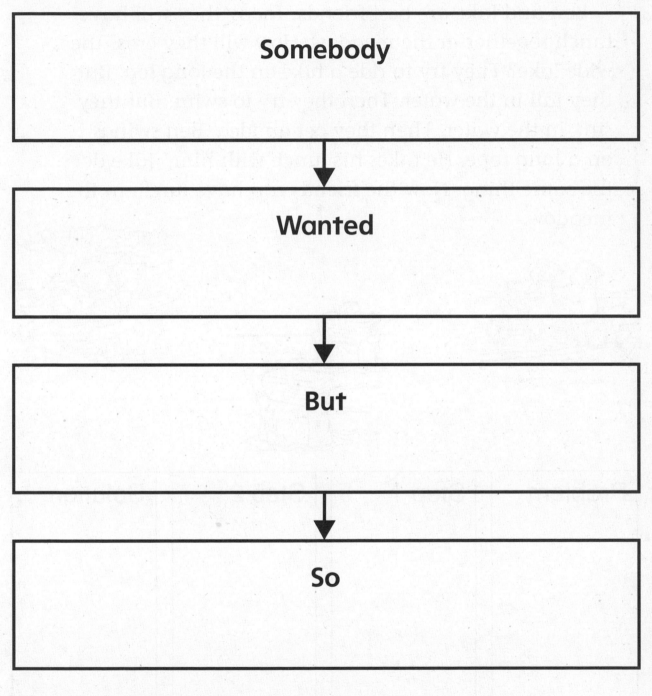

Somebody

↓

Wanted

↓

But

↓

So

How does the Problem and Solution Chart help you better understand <u>The Kite</u>?

 At Home: Have your child use the chart to retell the story.

The Kite • **Book 1.5/Unit 5** ⟨185⟩

Read the story about Ben and Jake. Then fill in the <u>problem</u> and <u>solution</u> chart.

Ben and Jake are best friends. Today they will have lunch together in the meadow. How will they cross the wide lake? They try to ride a bike on the long log. But they fall in the water. Then they try to swim. But they sink in the water. Then they get an idea. Ben swings on a long rope. He takes his lunch with him. Jake does the same thing. Now the friends can have lunch in the meadow.

Problem	Step 1	Step 2	Solution

 At Home: Have your child describe another problem and solution for Ben and Jake.

As I read, I will pay attention to vocabulary words.

	Today Cara Bear went with her mother and brother to
10	the beach.
12	Cara Bear loved the colorful umbrellas and beach
20	balls. The sky was a bright blue. The sand felt soft
31	under her feet. And the sun felt different than in the
42	meadow where she lived. Cara Bear was happy. She
51	started to write a new story.
57	I was swimming underwater. Everywhere I looked, I
65	could see beautiful fish. I could swim and I didn't even
76	need a tank to breathe. How amazing it all was!
86	Suddenly, I felt something tap my head. I turned and
96	saw the long arm of an octopus! I tried to shout, but I
109	couldn't hear the sound. 113

Comprehension Check

1. How is the beach different from the meadow where Cara Bear lives?

2. What animals does Cara Bear see with her imagination?

	Words Read	–	Number of Errors	=	Words Correct Score
First Read		–		=	
Second Read		–		=	

At Home: Help your child read the passage, paying attention to the goal at the top of the page.

© Macmillan/McGraw-Hill

Name _____

You can pick out the word parts of a word to figure out its meaning.

Circle the word that completes each sentence. Write <u>now</u> or <u>past</u> to tell about the action. Then write the base word of the word you circled.

1. Keisha (climbed, climbing) to the top of the slide.

_____

_ _

_____

2. She is (shouted, shouting) hello to Raffi.

_____

_ _

_____

3. He heard her voice and (waved, waving).

_____

_ _

_____

4. They both see Sal (jumping, jumped) in the pile of

_____

_ _

leaves. _____

5. Sal is (smiled, smiling) and having fun.

_____

_ _

_____

At Home: Talk about three things you did over the weekend. Pay attention to the verbs that end in -ed.

Add the ending to the word. Then use the word in a funny sentence about the picture.

1. wide + er = _____

_____

_____

2. strange + est = _____

_____

_____

3. brave + er = _____

_____

_____

4. large + er = _____

_____

_____

 At Home: Ask your child to make up a story about one of the pictures. Tell your child to use one or two of the words on the page in the story.

The Kite • **Book 1.5/Unit 5** ⟨189⟩

© Macmillan/McGraw-Hill

Name _____

Make a diagram. Draw a picture of an object. Write the name of the object. Then label each part.

 At Home: Have your child compare two things, such as pets, games, friends, or siblings. Help your child fill in a Venn Diagram with the information.

Name _____

Read the words in the box. Find them in the puzzle. Circle them.

fright	cry	mild	slid	bright	think	try

```
m  t  h  i  n  k  f  a
c  y  t  r  y  o  p  s
l  r  o  m  i  l  d  v
p  f  r  i  g  h  t  m
c  r  y  t  s  s  d  v
b  o  n  f  s  l  i  d
q  r  b  r  i  g  h  t
```

Think of a word with the <u>long i</u> sound, spelled <u>igh</u>, <u>i</u>, or <u>y</u>. Use it in a sentence.

_____

_ _ _ _ _ _ _ _ _ _ _ _ _ _ _ _ _

_____

Think of a word with the <u>short i</u> sound. Use it in a sentence.

_____

_ _ _ _ _ _ _ _ _ _ _ _ _ _ _ _ _

_____

© Macmillan/McGraw-Hill

At Home: Have your child think of words with the long *i* sound, spelled *i*, *y*, or *igh* and the short *i* sound. Help your child make up a silly sentence that uses some of the words.

Name _____

Draw a picture of each silly phrase.

1. A **shark** that **sparkles**.

2. An **arm** with a **charm**.

3. A **carp** in a **car**.

4. A **barn** with **bars**.

5. A **star** with a **scarf**.

6. A **farm** with **park**.

 At Home: Brainstorm *ar* words with your child. Can he or she think of a silly phrase using the *ar* words?

Read the clues. Then use words in the box to fill in the crossword puzzle.

round   better   children   or
machine   question   discovery

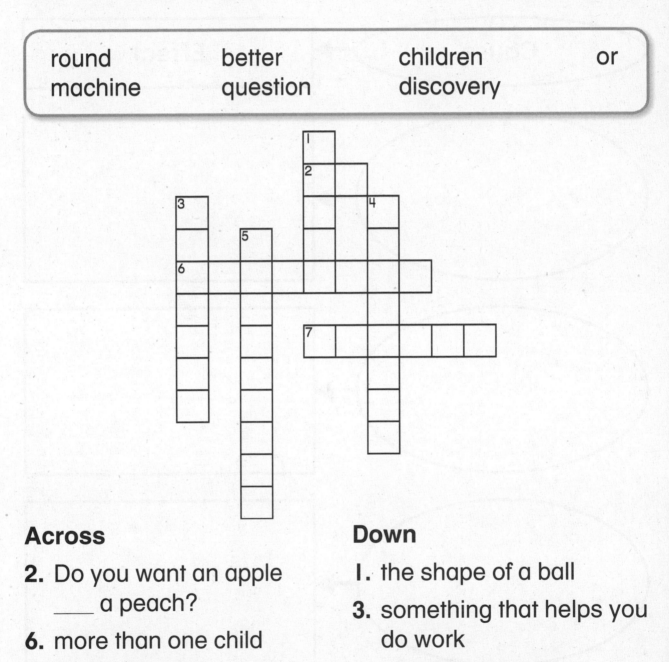

Across

2. Do you want an apple ____ a peach?

6. more than one child

7. The show was ____ this time than before

Down

1. the shape of a ball

3. something that helps you do work

4. You can ask this

5. something you find

 At Home: Encourage your child to draw a picture of a discovery he or she might make some day.

Name _____

As you read <u>Kids' Inventions</u>, fill in the Cause and Effect Chart.

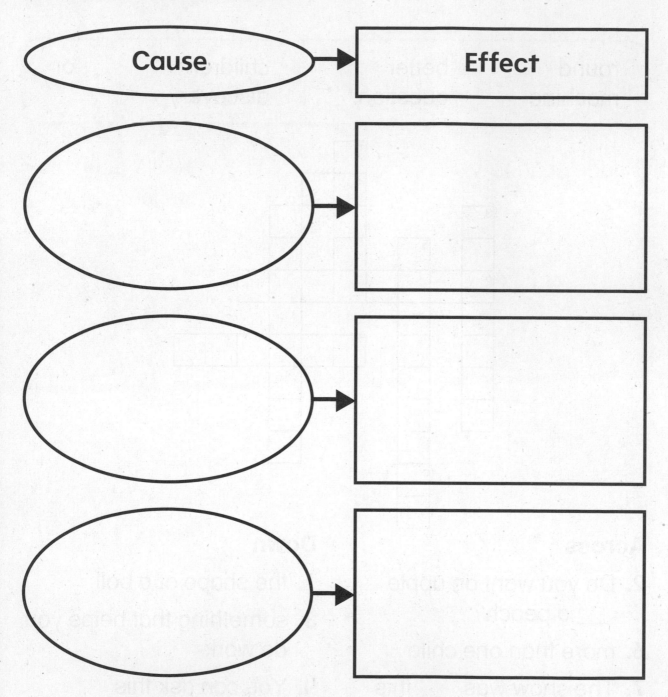

How does the Cause and Effect Chart help you better understand <u>Kids' Inventions</u>?

 At Home: Have your child use the chart to retell the story.

Name _____

The **cause** is why something happens.
The **effect** is what happens.

Match each cause to the correct effect.

cause

1. Jade is hungry.

2. It starts to rain.

3. Ray jumps out of the swing.

4. Emily's bike has a flat tire.

5. Morgan misses the bus.

6. The dog sees a cat.

effect

a. Matt will put up his umbrella.

b. She puts air in the tire.

c. She will eat an apple.

d. She gets a ride to school from her mom.

e. The dog barks loudly.

f. He scrapes his arm.

Read the cause. Then write an effect.

7. It is very hot outside.

_____

_ _

_____

 At Home: Let your child choose one sentence to illustrate.

Words with the same or almost the same meaning are **synonyms**. You can use a **dictionary** or a **thesaurus** to find synonyms.

Choose a synonym from the box for the <u>underlined</u> word. Write the synonym on the line.

award	begin	act	contest	smart

1. Jessica has a <u>clever</u> puppy. _____

2. The puppy likes to <u>perform</u>. _____

3. They will <u>start</u> practicing tomorrow. _____

4. The puppy was the best act in the _____

<u>competition</u>. _____

5. The puppy won a <u>prize</u>. _____

At Home: Find two synonyms for *funny*. Write a sentence using *funny*. Say the sentence using the synonyms.

© Macmillan/McGraw-Hill

As I read, I will pay attention to pauses for punctuation.

	Long ago, taking pictures was hard work for the
9	photographer. Cameras were very heavy machines.
15	They were hard to hold or carry. Cameras often weighed
25	more than 50 pounds and usually rested on
32	three-legged stands.
34	At that time, there was no film either. Pictures were
44	taken on heavy glass plates. The plates had to be
54	kept in the dark, or the photographer could not print
64	photographs from them.
67	Some people thought that there had to be a better
77	and easier way to take pictures. George Eastman found
88	that way.
90	In 1884, film had been invented. Now a picture could be
100	captured on film, instead of on a glass plate. 109

Comprehension Check

1. Was taking pictures harder to do before 1884?

2. Why did George Eastman invent film?

	Words Read	–	Number of Errors	=	Words Correct Score
First Read		–		=	
Second Read		–		=	

© Macmillan/McGraw-Hill

At Home: Help your child read the passage, paying attention to the goal at the top of the page.

Look at the book cover. Then fill in the missing information on the card catalog page.

Adam's Time Machine

Mary Thompson

Electronic Card Catalog

SEARCH

Call Number J FICT
Author _____
Title _____
Publisher Young Publishing, New York, © 2002
Subject Inventions -- Fiction
Friendship -- Fiction
Time-Travel -- Fiction
Adventure -- Fiction
Summary Adam builds a time machine and travels back in time to meet famous inventors including Ben Franklin, Benjamin Banneker, and Thomas Edison.

Use the card catalog page to answer the questions.

1. When was the book published? _____

2. What is the call number? _____

3. Is this book fiction of nonfiction? _____

4. What subjects can you read about in this book?

_____

_____

At Home: Help your child make a card catalog page for his or her favorite story.

© Macmillan/McGraw-Hill

Name _____

An **abbreviation** is a short form of writing a longer word.

Mister → **Mr.**   Saturday → **Sat.**   Doctor → **Dr.**

Read each sentence. Find the mistake.
Write the sentence correctly.

1. Mr James is the soccer coach for our team.

_____

- -

_____

2. When Tom broke his leg, dr Cage put the cast on it.

_____

- -

_____

3. Do you know mr. Willem's address?

_____

- -

_____

4. On sat, my mom and I baked cookies together.

_____

- -

_____

© Macmillan/McGraw-Hill

At Home: Help your child search for magazine pictures to
match the abbreviations Mr., Mrs., and Dr.

Name _____

bark	carp	car	garden
star	park	harp	shark

Use the words in the box to complete the sentences.

_____

1. It has a tail and a fin. _____

2. Plants grow in this. _____

3. You can play it. _____

4. You can drive it in the rain. _____

5. You can play a ball game here. _____

6. A man can catch this. _____

7. This sparkles in the sky. _____

8. This is what a dog does. _____

At Home: Help your child makes riddles for these words: *alarm*, *scarf* and *farm*.

Name _____

Read the words in the box. Find them in the puzzle. Circle the words.

forty	short	born	sort
sport	form	port	north

```
p  b  o  r  n  m  v  p
o  s  h  o  r  t  s  o
r  s  p  j  g  x  d  t
t  o  n  o  r  t  h  f
x  r  k  z  b  j  n  o
q  t  s  p  o  r  t  r
z  p  f  o  r  t  y  m
```

Write a sentence with the word <u>for</u>.

_____

- -

_____

Think of another <u>or</u> word. Write a sentence using that word.

_____

- -

_____

At Home: Have your child find pictures in a magazine of things that have the *or* sound.

Whistle for Willie • **Book 1.5/Unit 5** 201

Use words from the box to complete the story.

early	instead	suddenly	along
errand	nothing	thought	

Mr. Stork went on an _____. He set out

_____ in the morning. He walked

_____ the path by the river. He

_____ he would be safe. _____,

Mr. Stork saw Mrs. Fox waiting in the bushes. He flew

along the river _____. Mr. Stork was

safe, and _____ happened.

At Home: Have your child create three sentences using words from the box.

**As you read <u>Whistle for Willie</u>, fill in the
Inference Chart.**

Text Clues	What You Know	Inferences

**How does the Inference Chart help you better
understand <u>Whistle for Willie</u>?**

 At Home: Have your child use the chart to retell the story.

© Macmillan/McGraw-Hill

Read the story.
Then choose the answer that completes each sentence.

Tory and Art played a game in the park. Art kicked the ball to Tory. Tory stopped the ball. Then she kicked it into the goal. Their team cheered. After the game, all the children had snacks. Art and Tory went to bed very early.

1. Tory and Art played _____.

○ on a soccer team   ○ football   ○ at school

2. When Tory made a goal, the team was _____.

○ bored   ○ sad   ○ happy

3. After the game, the children were _____.

○ hungry   ○ crying   ○ funny

4. Tory went to bed early because _____.

○ she ate too many snacks   ○ she was very tired   ○ she cheered for her team

© Macmillan/McGraw-Hill

 At Home: Ask your child to predict whether Art went to bed early, too, and to explain why or why not.

As I read, I will pay attention to pauses for punctuation.

	"I'll help," said Mom. "I will run along and hold
10	the bike."
12	Scott started to pedal down the street. Suddenly, the
21	bike picked up speed. Scott lifted his feet. Then he
31	slammed on the brakes. Mom caught him just before
40	he fell again.
43	"That's it," said Scott. "Nothing can help me. I
52	thought I could ride this bike, but I can't."
61	A few seconds later, Scott's friend, Dan came along.
70	Scott told Dan about his problem riding his new bike.
80	"I know what will help. But first I have a little errand
92	to do. I will be back soon," Dan said, smiling.
102	In a few minutes, Dan came back with his bike
112	and helmet. He had a shopping bag, too. Inside there
122	were skateboard kneepads, elbow pads, and wrist guards.
130	Dan told Scott to put them all on. 138

Comprehension Check

1. What is Scott having trouble doing?

2. How does Dan try to help Scott?

	Words Read	–	Number of Errors	=	Words Correct Score
First Read		–		=	
Second Read		–		=	

At Home: Help your child read the passage, paying attention to the goal at the top of the page.

© Macmillan/McGraw-Hill

Name _____

> A **base word** is the word that is left when you remove the **-ed** or **-ing** ending.
>
> James is **practicing** how to catch fly balls.
>
> The base word is **practice**. Notice that some verbs are made by removing the final **e** before adding **-ing** or **-ed**.
>
> **practice** to do something over and over to get better at doing it.

Write the base word for each word.

1. visited _____

2. explored _____

3. pressing _____

4. escaping _____

Choose two base words from above. Use each one in a sentence.

_____

_____

_____

_____

At Home: Say two sentences using the words explore and explored.

Read each verb. If the verb was formed by changing the final y to i before adding ed, circle the word. Then color the spaces with the circled verbs.

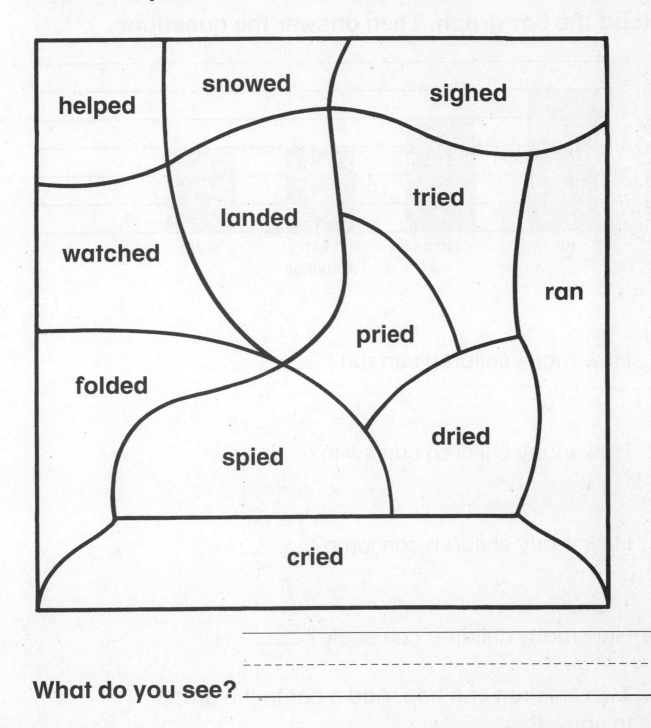

helped

snowed

sighed

tried

landed

watched

ran

pried

folded

dried

spied

cried

_____

- -

What do you see? _____

 At Home: Have your child write and illustrate a sentence about something he or she has tried.

Whistle for Willie • **Book 1.5/Unit 5** 207

A **graph** can show how many of something.

Read the bar graph. Then answer the questions.

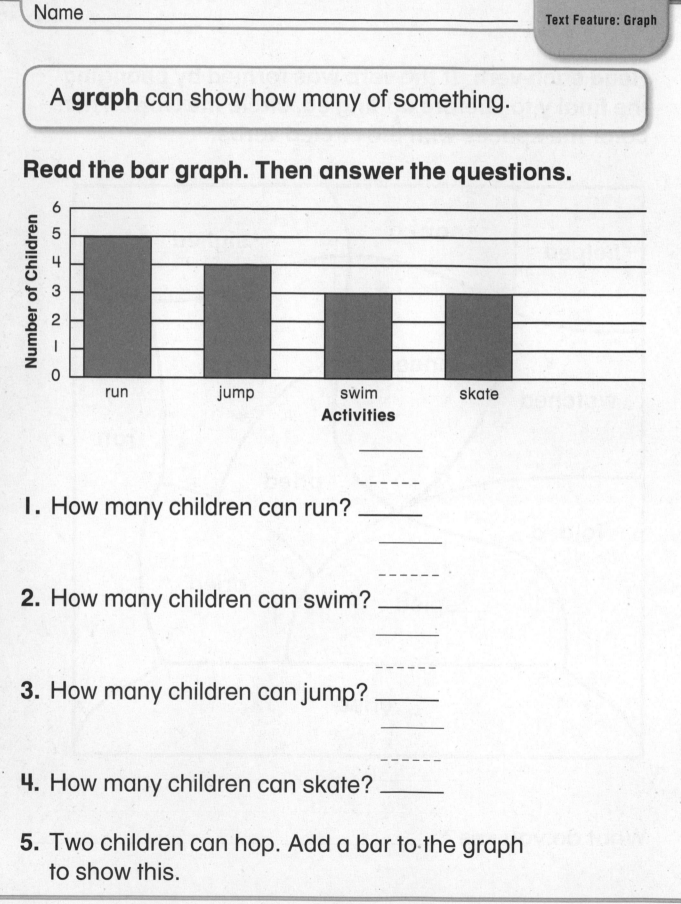

Number of Children

6
5
4
3
2
1
0

run   jump   swim   skate

Activities

_____

- - - - -

1. How many children can run? _____

_____

- - - - -

2. How many children can swim? _____

_____

- - - - -

3. How many children can jump? _____

_____

- - - - -

4. How many children can skate? _____

5. Two children can hop. Add a bar to the graph to show this.

At Home: Have your child ask family members about things they can do. Ask your child to make a bar graph showing the information.

Use an <u>ar</u> word or an <u>or</u> word to answer each clue.

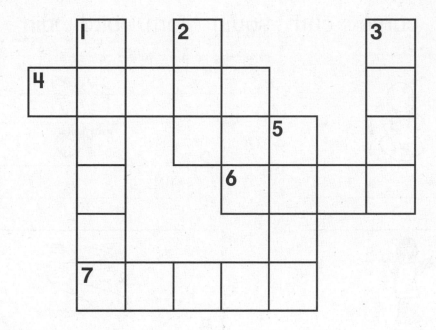

Across

4. a fish with big teeth

6. You eat with this

7. A blizzard is a kind of this

Down

1. You wear these in the summer.

2. throw with this

3. a place to play

5. the shape of something

 At Home: Play *ar, or* Tic Tac Toe with your child. Make a Tic Tac Toe grid. Players write words with either *ar* or *or* in the boxes.

Whistle for Willie • **Book 1.5/Unit 5** **209**

Name _____

Use a word from the box to name each picture. Circle the letters that stand for the sound you hear in <u>turn</u>.

purse	curve	curl	squirt	fern	bird	girl	perch

1. _____

2. _____

3. _____

4. _____

5. _____

6. _____

7. _____

8. _____

At Home: Have your child spell the words in the box without looking at the page.

© Macmillan/McGraw-Hill

Read the clues. Write words from the box to fill in the puzzle.

animals	beautiful	crowded	from
part	places	ground	tiny

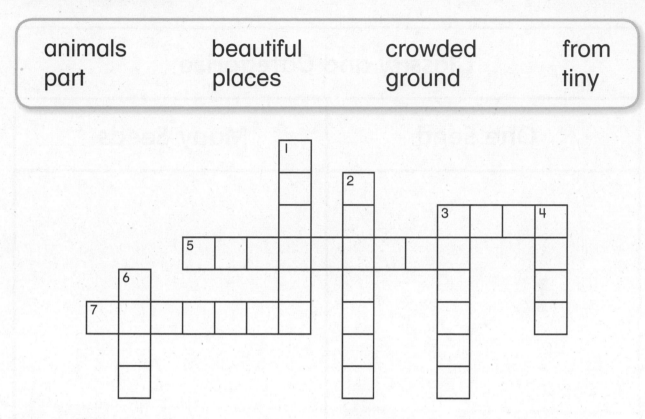

Across

3. not whole

5. very pretty

7. too full

Down

1. land

2. dogs, cats, birds

3. where you go

4. very small

6. go ____ here to there

Name _____

As you read A Fruit is a Suitcase for Seeds, fill in the Classify and Categorize Chart

Classify and Categorize	
One Seed	**Many Seeds**

How does the Classify and Categorize Chart help you better understand A Fruit is a Suitcase for Seeds?

 At Home: Have your child use the chart to retell the story.

Name _____

Look at the pictures in each group. Write a name for the group.

1. _____

2. _____

3. _____

4. _____

5. _____

6. _____

At Home: Ask your child to categorize household objects, using categories such as *silverware* or *things that belong in the bedroom.*

Name _____

As I read, I will pay attention to patterns in the passage.

9	Cranberries grow on vines with tiny leaves that curl up on the stems.
13	Cranberry vines are evergreen plants. Evergreens stay
20	green through all the seasons. Their leaves do change
29	colors or die in the winter.
35	Cranberries grow in the northern part of the United
44	States. Some grow wild, but most are planted and
53	grown by farmers for food.
58	Cranberries grow in bogs. A bog is a place where the
69	ground is soft and wet.
74	Cranberries need a lot of rain to grow, about an inch
85	of water every week. Bogs are wonderful places for
94	cranberries, because they get a lot of rain. The
103	ground in a bog has sandy soil, which is also good for
115	growing cranberries. 117

Comprehension Check

1. What does evergreen mean?

2. What is the ground and soil like in a bog?

	Words Read	–	Number of Errors	=	Words Correct Score
First Read		–		=	
Second Read		–		=	

◇ 214 **A Fruit Is a Suitcase for Seeds**
Book 1.5/Unit 5

At Home: Help your child read the passage, paying attention to the goal at the top of the page.

© Macmillan/McGraw-Hill

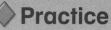

Name _____

Read each sentence. Use the context clues to figure out the meaning of the <u>underlined</u> word. Write its meaning.

1. Often when our family travels by bus, there are many <u>passengers</u>. Some people even have to stand.

_____

- -

_____

2. We also travel by car. We <u>snack</u> on fruit. We bring other treats to eat, too.

_____

- -

_____

3. When we fly on a plane, we bring a lot of <u>luggage</u>. Each person packs his or her own suitcase.

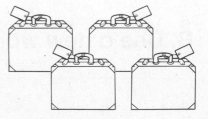

_____

- -

_____

At Home: Talk about items you would pack into a suitcase if you were to travel on a vacation.

Name _____

A. Add the prefixes <u>re-</u> or <u>un-</u> to the words in the box. Write the new words.

| tie   tell   happy   pack   true   load   safe |

1. _____   2. _____

3. _____   4. _____

5. _____   6. _____

7. _____   8. _____

9. _____   10. _____

B. Use a new word from above in a sentence.

_____

_____

At Home: Have your child look for words with the prefixes *re-* and *un-* in print materials such as magazines, books, or mail.

© Macmillan/McGraw-Hill

In some poems, the second line of a verse rhymes
with the fourth line.

**A. Finish the poem. Write a word that rhymes
with the word at the end of the second line.**

Here comes Johnny Appleseed!
He walks around and **around**,
And where he goes, he leaves behind

_____

- -

Little trees growing out of the _____.

**B. Work with a partner to write a new poem. Make
the second and fourth lines rhyme.**

_____
- -
_____
- -
_____
- -
_____
- -
_____

At Home: Look through a poetry book with
your child or recite a favorite poem. Ask your
child to tell which words rhyme.

A Fruit Is a Suitcase for Seeds
Book I.5/Unit 5
 217

Name _____

Play with a partner. Draw lines to make words with the letters <u>ar</u>, <u>or</u>, <u>er</u>, <u>ur</u>, or <u>ir</u>. Take turns. Write the words on the lines.

b   t

     ar

ch   p

     er

t   st

     ir

h   m

     or

sh   d

     ur

st   n

How many words did you make?

_____

You: _____

_____

Your partner: _____

_____ **chart**

_____ _____

_____ _____

_____ _____

_____ _____

_____ _____

_____ _____

_____ _____

_____ _____

_____ _____

_____ _____

_____ _____

© Macmillan/McGraw-Hill

 At Home: Ask your child to name some of the words he or she made.

Name _____

Write the word from the box that has the opposite meaning.

1. hate _____

2. huge _____

3. all _____

4. adults _____

5. always _____

6. late _____

7. crying _____

8. whole _____

nothing
part
love
children
tiny
early
laughter
never

Look at the pictures. Read the sentences. Then match the pictures with the sentences below. Number the pictures with the correct sentence.

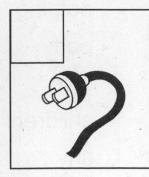  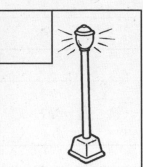 

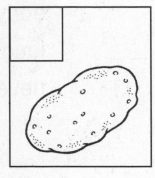  

1. Perhaps you'll find this along a road.

2. This might be part of a machine.

3. You should find these in a meadow.

4. This is supposed to be on a boat.

5. Gold is a terrific discovery!

6. Children like this baked or mashed.

7. This is far from us in the sky.

Read the words in the box.
Find them in the puzzle. Then circle them.

frown	found	out	mouth	house
plow	now	round	clown	ground

```
h a m o p l o w
g h o n m c u x
r o u n d l t f
o u t u x o c r
u s h l r w l o
n e f o u n d w
d n o w o f x n
```

Use words from the box in sentences.

_____

- -

_____

- -

_____

- -

_____

- -

 At Home: Write *-oud, -ound, -ouse, -out, -ow,* and *-own* on separate cards. Take turns picking cards and filling in letters to create new words. Examples: *-oud, cloud; -ound, found.*

Dot and Jabber and the Big Bug
Mystery • **Book 1.5/Unit 6**

 221

Use the words in the box to complete the story.

been	gone	searching	other	clues	invisible

_____

My grandmother has _____ reading a mystery.

It is about a detective and an _____ man.

A detective needs _____ to find a man

he can't see. The detective saw footprints when he was

_____ the beach. When he reached the water,

the footprints were _____ . The detective was

tricked again! He has to look for _____ clues.

At Home: Ask your child to tell you a story about a mystery.
Then write it out together.

As you read Dot and Jabber and the Big Bug Mystery, fill in the Illustrations Chart.

Use Illustrations	
Illustration	**What It Shows**

How does the Illustrations Chart help you better understand Dot and Jabber and the Big Bug Mystery?

At Home: Have your child use the chart to retell the story.

Dot and Jabber and the Big Bug
Mystery • **Book I.5/Unit 6**   223

© Macmillan/McGraw-Hill

Draw a picture of an insect in the box. Include details about the insect.

Write about the insect. Tell at least 4 interesting facts.

_____

1. _____

2. _____

3. _____

4. _____

Dot and Jabber and the Big Bug Mystery • Book 1.5/Unit 6

At Home: Ask your child to find a picture of an insect in a magazine or book. Help him or her make up several sentences about the picture.

Name _____

As I read, I will pay attention to exclamations.

	The next day the family went for corn treats. Nell
10	ate so much, she thought she would burst.
18	On the way back, Nell and Susie stopped to look
28	at caterpillars crawling on milkweed plants.
34	"They've grown!" said Nell.
38	"That's because they ate so many leaves,"
45	explained Susie. "Caterpillars eat a lot and grow
53	so big that their skin pops. They grow new skins!"
63	"Wow!" said Nell, but "Where are all
70	the butterflies?"
72	That night, there was a starlit sky and a full
82	moon. Susie invited Nell outside to look for
90	caterpillars. They brought flashlights, and Susie's
96	mom came, too. 99

Comprehension Check

1. What happens to caterpillars when they eat a lot?

2. What do caterpillars eat?

	Words Read	−	Number of Errors	=	Words Correct Score
First Read		−		=	
Second Read		−		=	

At Home: Help your child read the passage, paying attention to the goal at the top of the page.

Dot and Jabber and the Big Bug
Mystery • **Book 1.5/Unit 6**

> A **dictionary** gives the meaning of a word and shows how to use the word in a sentence.

Complete each dictionary entry by writing a sentence that uses the bolded word.

deliver to take or carry something to a person or a place:

_____

_ _

_____

detective a person who looks for clues to solve a mystery:

_____

_ _

_____

explore to search or look into carefully:

_____

_ _

_____

insect an animal with 3 body parts, 6 legs, and no backbone:

_____

_ _

_____

solve to figure out:

_____

_ _

_____

 At Home: Ask your child to draw a picture to go with one of the sentences on this page and write a caption using one of the vocabulary words.

Connect a word part from each column to make a real word. Write the words you make on the lines.

bas	bit
ham	cil
kit	ket
les	kin
mag	mer
nap	net
pen	son
rab	ten

1. _____

2. _____

3. _____

4. _____

5. _____

6. _____

7. _____

8. _____

At Home: Write the word parts above on separate cards. Have your child pick two cards at a time and figure out if the word parts can be put together to make a real word.

Dot and Jabber and the Big Bug Mystery • **Book 1.5/Unit 6**

227

© Macmillan/McGraw-Hill

Name _____

Write an article about your favorite insect.
Use the heads as a guide.

Name of Insect _____

What the Insect Looks Like

_____

- -

_____

- -

_____

Where the Insect Lives

_____

- -

_____

- -

_____

What the Insect Eats

_____

- -

_____

 At Home: Look at an online encyclopedia. Help your child
find the entry for "insect." Read appropriate sections of the
article to your child and discuss the new information learned.

Name _____

Write one or two letters in each blank to make a word. Write sentences using some of the words.

1. _____ ound   _____ ound   _____ ound

_____

- -

2. _____ own   _____ own   _____ own

_____

- -

3. _____ oat   _____ oat   _____ oat

_____

- -

4. _____ ird   _____ ird

_____

- -

At Home: Have your child make other words using the spelling patterns above. Write the words in a list.

Dot and Jabber and the Big Bug
Mystery • **Book 1.5/Unit 6**   **229**

Complete each sentence by writing a word that rhymes with the word in bold print.

stood	cook	foot	look	hoof	shook

_____

1. He has **soot** on his _____.

_____

2. The _____ hung the pot on a **hook**.

_____

3. The cat _____ on the **hood**.

_____

4. _____ at that big **book**!

_____

5. The horse stamped his _____ and the dog said **woof**.

_____

6. **Look** at how the tree _____!

 At Home: Have your child use two words from the box in a rhyming sentence.

© Macmillan/McGraw-Hill

Read each riddle. Write the answer on the line.

bird	Earth	table	bear
fooling	guess	helmet	space

1. You don't know? Do this. _____

2. Put this on your head. _____

3. My young are called cubs. _____

4. My young are called chicks. _____

5. I have four legs. _____

6. I'm just kidding. _____

7. I am full of dirt. _____

8. I am between here and Mars. _____

 At Home: Help your child make up other riddles for the words in the box.

Little Bear Goes to the Moon
Book 1.5/Unit 6
 231

© Macmillan/McGraw-Hill

Name _____

As you read <u>Little Bear Goes to the Moon</u>, fill in the Predictions Chart.

What I Predict	What Happens

How does the Predictions Chart help you better understand <u>Little Bear Goes to the Moon</u>?

At Home: Have your child use the chart to retell the story.

Look at each picture. Predict what will happen next. Draw a picture and write a sentence.

1. _____

_ _

_____

2. _____

_ _

_____

3. _____

_ _

_____

4. _____

_ _

_____

© Macmillan/McGraw-Hill

At Home: Ask your child to write a prediction of what will happen next week.

As I read, I will pay attention to pauses for punctuation.

	"My Pluto 3000 will never keep up with your new bike,"
10	said Rick.
12	"You'll just pedal faster," said Rose. "Anyway, I would
21	never leave you behind. Friends don't do that."
29	"Let's bring along some lunch," suggested Rick.
36	There were delicious things on the table to choose from.
46	They took some bottles of orange water that were on the
57	table, too.
59	"We better put our roam-from-home beepers on our
69	shoes," said Rose. "Better safe than sorry, she added.
78	"Then if we get lost, our families will be able to find us."
91	"And don't forget your bike light," said Rick.
100	"Of course not," said Rose. "We can't go anywhere with
108	without bike lights." I I I

Comprehension Check

1. What do Rose and Rick do to prepare for their long bike ride?

2. Do you think Rose and Rick will be traveling safely on their trip?

	Words Read	–	Number of Errors	=	Words Correct Score
First Read		–		=	
Second Read		–		=	

© Macmillan/McGraw-Hill

 At Home: Help your child read the passage, paying attention to the goal at the top of the page.

Context clues are words that help you figure out the meaning of a new word. Context clues may be found in the same sentence or in nearby sentences.

Write the letter of the correct meaning of each underlined word. Use context clues.

a. something that protects a person's head

b. the ground; also the planet where we live

c. dropped, rolled

d. being silly

e. the place where astronauts travel

1. My uncle took me to a museum about astronauts and <u>space</u>. _____

2. I wore an astronaut's <u>helmet</u> and sat in a real rocket ship. _____

3. The heavy helmet <u>tumbled</u> to the floor when I took it off my head. _____

4. My uncle likes making jokes and <u>fooling</u> around with me when we go places. _____

5. He told my Mom, "It's good to feel the <u>earth</u> under my feet after that trip to the moon!" _____

© Macmillan/McGraw-Hill

 At Home: Ask your child to make up sentences using three of the words in bold letters.

Little Bear Goes to the Moon
Book 1.5/Unit 6

235

Pick a word from the box. Then add the suffix -ful or -less to answer each question.

| harm | care | thought | hope | help | friend |

1. He took his time to do his work well.

What was he? _____

2. She is always thinking of others.

What is she? _____

3. They gave up and didn't even try.

What were they? _____

4. That won't hurt you at all.

What is it? _____

5. No one seems to care about him.

What is he? _____

6. They always try to do something

for you. What are they? _____

At Home: Ask your child to look through a favorite book and find words with the suffixes *-ful* and *-less*.

Name _____

Look at each picture. Write a question and an answer about the picture.
Then draw a line from the question and the answer to the person to show who is speaking.

_____

- -

1. Question: _____

_____

- -

2. Answer: _____

_____

- -

3. Question: _____

_____

- -

4. Answer: _____

At Home: Have your child think of a question to ask
someone in the picture and to predict the answer. Together,
write out the question and answer.

Little Bear Goes to the Moon
Book 1.5/Unit 6

237

© Macmillan/McGraw-Hill

Complete the puzzle.

The answer to each clue has the vowel sounds <u>oo</u>, <u>ou</u>, or <u>ow</u>.

Across
1. We get milk from this animal.
2. You can read this.
3. A queen wears this.
5. not quiet
6. not up

Down
1. He makes you laugh.
4. This is a shape.
5. to glance at
7. the opposite of in

 At Home: Have your child use each answer in another sentence.

Name _____

Use a word with the <u>oo</u> sound to name each picture.

1. _____

2. _____

3. _____

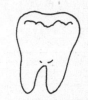

4. _____

5. _____

Draw pictures for two other words with the same <u>oo</u> sound.

 At Home: Have your child draw pictures for the incorrect *oo* words in the sentences and label them.

Name _____

Write a sentence for each picture using one or more of the words.

Try to use all the words in the box at least one time.

only laugh goes ever ordinary interesting

_____

- -

1. _____

_____

- -

2. _____

_____

- -

3. _____

_____

- -

4. _____

Try to use all left over words in one sentence.

_____

- -

_____

At Home: Ask your child to tell a funny story about one of the pictures. Help him or her write the story.

© Macmillan/McGraw-Hill

As you read Cool Jobs, fill in the Classify and Catagorize Chart.

Classify and Categorize	
Jobs to Make Things	**Jobs That Help**

How does the Classify and Catagorize Chart help you better understand Cool Jobs?

 At Home: Have your child use the chart to retell the story.

Name _____

Sort the words into two groups. Write a name for each group on the line.

cook   school   vet   house   park

teacher   store   actor   sailor   playground

_____

Name: _____

_____

_____

_____

_____

_____

_____

_____

 At Home: Have your child draw a map to show
and to label the places he or she listed.

Name _____

Read the sentence. Circle the antonym for the underlined word. Then use the antonym in a new sentence.

1. I want to see my favorite baseball player hit a <u>few</u> home runs at the game.

      zero   many   ball

_____

- -

_____

2. Sometimes the bat will <u>break</u>.

      fix   smash   hide

- -

_____

3. The seats in the ballpark are <u>clean</u>.

      dirty   blue   hard

_____

- -

_____

4. We all <u>laugh</u> when our team wins.

      cry   waves   crawls

_____

- -

_____

© Macmillan/McGraw-Hill

At Home: Use some of the antonyms to
make up a silly sentence.

As I read, I will pay attention to patterns.

	Many different workers are needed to finish a building.
9	All of them follow the architect's plans.
16	• Electricians put in the electric wires and lights.
24	• Plumbers put in the water pipes.
30	• Carpenters build things made of wood.
36	• Painters paint the walls.
40	• Landscapers fill the yard with grass, trees, and other
49	plants.
50	Architects watch closely as each part of a structure
59	is built. They visit the building often. They make sure
69	everyone follows the designs. You need special training
77	to become an architect. You must go to college for five
88	or six years. There, you learn all about how to plan
99	a building. 101

Comprehension Check

1. What does a landscaper do?

2. Who designs the plans for a building?

	Words Read	−	Number of Errors	=	Words Correct Score
First Read		−		=	
Second Read		−		=	

At Home: Help your child read the passage, paying attention to the goal at the top of the page.

Search the Media Center

Back Forward Stop Refresh Home

Address

Google   weather.com   Yahoo!   Chicago Cubs : The Official Site

Web Search | Bee Keeper | | Go |

Read each sentence. Then write the key words you would type in the search box.

1. You want to find out about a job with animals other than a beekeeper.

_____

- -

_____

2. You want to know more about one of the planets.

_____

- -

_____

3. You want to find out about a kind of machine.

_____

- -

_____

4. You want to find out about the person who wrote your favorite book.

_____

- -

_____

At Home: If possible, help your child search and read about one of the above topics on the Web.

Name _____

Add one or more letters in the box to *oo* to make different words like <u>moon</u>.

| b | d | f | r | t | l |

_____ _____ _____

- -

_____ _____ _____

- -

_____ _____ _____

| c | h | l | m | p | s | t |

_____ _____ _____

- -

_____ _____ _____

- -

_____ _____ _____

- -

_____ _____ _____

Draw a picture that includes five or more of the words.

┌───┐
│   │
│   │
│   │
│   │
│   │
│   │
└───┘

At Home: Have your child make up a story using a few words they made from each box. Help your child write the story.

Complete the puzzle with words that have <u>ou</u>, <u>ow</u>, or <u>oo</u>.

Across

1. to cry out in pain like a wolf

2. how you get a ball in a hoop

5 a word that means "also"

6 part of a house

8. how you sound when you root for a team

9. what you swim in

Down

1. the sound an owl makes

2. a ball of ice cream

3. what you use to fix things

4. part of a coat that goes on a head

7. the sound a cow makes

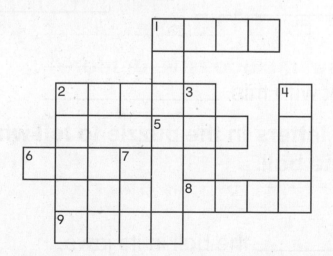

At Home: Have your child make up a crossword puzzle using words with *oo* as in room.

Cool Jobs • **Book 1.5/Unit 6** 247

A. Use words from the box to fill the puzzle.

haul	chalk	straw	taught	wall	hawk

1. You can write with this. _____

2. part of a room _____

3. a way to carry things _____

4. something a teacher did

_____

_____

5. a large bird _____

6. You can sip milk with this. _____

B. Use the boxed letters in the puzzle to tell what happened to the ball.

_____

The dog _____ the ball in its jaws.

At Home: Have your child write more puzzle clues for words that rhyme with *chalk*, *saw*, and *wall*.

Find the words in the puzzle and circle them. Then write a sentence for each word.

| wild | learn | enough | across | air | cubs | eyes |

```
X Q Z A C R O S S
E N O U G H P F E
B J F D B Q Z X Y
A C L E A R N P E
I G W I L D C R S
R X G H C U B S D
```

Write three sentences using words from the box.

1. _____

2. _____

3. _____

At Home: Have your child make his or her own puzzle for someone at home to solve.

A Tiger Cub Grows Up
Book 1.5/Unit 6

249

Name _____

As you read A Tiger Cub Grows Up, fill in the Compare and Contrast Chart.

Compare and Contrast	
Cub	**Grown-up**

How does the Compare and Contrast Chart help you better understand A Tiger Cub Grows Up?

 At Home: Have your child use the chart to retell the story.

Name _____

When you **compare**, you tell how things are alike.

When you **contrast**, you tell how things are different.

You have read "A Tiger Grows Up" and "The Tiger". Both are about a tiger. The two tigers are alike in some ways. They are different in many ways.

Write three things about the tiger from the poem and three things about the tiger from the story. Circle the things that are alike. Underline the things that are different.

"The Tiger"

by Douglas Florian

_____

– – – – – – – – – – – – – – – – –

1. _____

_____

– – – – – – – – – – – – – – – – –

2. _____

– – – – – – – – – – – – – – – – –

3. _____

"A Tiger Grows Up"

by Joan Hewitt

_____

– – – – – – – – – – – – – – – – –

1. _____

_____

– – – – – – – – – – – – – – – – –

2. _____

– – – – – – – – – – – – – – – – –

3. _____

 At Home: Have your child write a sentence about one way the tigers are alike.

As I read, I will pay attention to pauses for punctuation.

	A baby bottlenose dolphin swims as soon as it is born.
11	There is so much more the baby dolphin will learn to do
23	in the first hour of life! The dolphin baby is called a calf.
36	The calf must swim to the surface of the water to
47	breathe. Sometimes the mother will help push the
55	newborn up for its first gulp of air. Next, the calf must
67	learn to drink milk. The newborn baby dolphin is about
77	3 feet long and weighs about 30 pounds. Its mother's
85	milk helps the dolphin grow quickly. In just two months,
95	the calf will weigh twice as much. When the dolphin is
106	all grown, it can be from 8 to 12 feet long and weigh up
118	to 1,000 pounds. 120

Comprehension Check

1. What do calves need to learn?

2. How big is a newborn dolphin?

	Words Read	–	Number of Errors	=	Words Correct Score
First Read		–		=	
Second Read		–		=	

© Macmillan/McGraw-Hill

 At Home: Help your child read the passage, paying attention to the goal at the top of the page.

Write the base word. Then write a sentence using the inflected verb.

1. opened

_____

- - - - - - - - - - - - - - - - - - -

_____

_____

2. chewing

_____

- - - - - - - - - - - - - - - - - - -

_____

_____

3. pointed

_____

- - - - - - - - - - - - - - - - - - -

_____

_____

4. tearing

_____

- - - - - - - - - - - - - - - - - - -

_____

At Home: As your child reads to you, occasionally point out verbs ending in *-ed* and *-ing*. Ask your child to identify the base words.

A Tiger Cub Grows Up
Book 1.5/Unit 6

 253

Name _____

Write a paragraph about a tiger cub. Use words from the box in your paragraph.

caught	crawl	tall	paw	claws

_____

- - - - - - - - - - - - - - - -

_____

_____

- - - - - - - - - - - - - - - -

_____

_____

- - - - - - - - - - - - - - - -

_____

_____

- - - - - - - - - - - - - - - -

_____

_____

- - - - - - - - - - - - - - - -

_____

 At Home: Have your child read his or her paragraph to you.

Name _____

Poets often use words in fun and interesting ways.
The sounds of words can help express their meaning.

Read the poem. Circle the sound words at the end of each verse. Then write your own words on the lines.

She'll Be Coming Round the Mountain

She'll be coming round the mountain

when she comes,

Chug, chug!

_____

- - - - - - - - - - - - - - - - - - - -

_____

She'll be driving six white horses

when she comes,

Whoa back!

_____

- - - - - - - - - - - - - - - - - - - -

_____

She'll be wearing red pajamas

when she comes,

Scratch, scratch!

_____

- - - - - - - - - - - - - - - - - - - -

_____

 At Home: Have your child read the poem aloud with you.
Then have your child read the poem again, substituting his
or her own sound words.

A Tiger Cub Grows Up
Book 1.5/Unit 6

 255

© Macmillan/McGraw-Hill

Name _____

Play Concentration

Cut out the rhyming word card pairs. Mix them up
and put them face down on a desk or on the floor.
With a partner, take turns turning over two cards.
Read each card. If they have the same vowel
sound and rhyme, keep the cards. If they don't
match, return them to their places.

caught	taught	saw	paw
lawn	yawn	cook	look
moon	soon	fool	tool

 At Home: Play Concentration with your child.

Name _____

Use the letters to make new words. You can use letters more than once.

| t | b | l | c | s | j | br |

1. _____ oy

2. _____ oy

3. _____ oy

4. _____ oi _____

5. _____ oi _____

6. _____ oi _____

7. _____ oi _____

8. **Write a sentence about the picture. Use some of the words you made.**

_____

_____

_____

_____

© Macmillan/McGraw-Hill

 At Home: Have your child write more words. Ask your child to use the letters *oi* or *oy* in his or her words.

Use words from the box to fill in the puzzle.

grew	leave	toward	circle
welcoming	toppled	wreck	

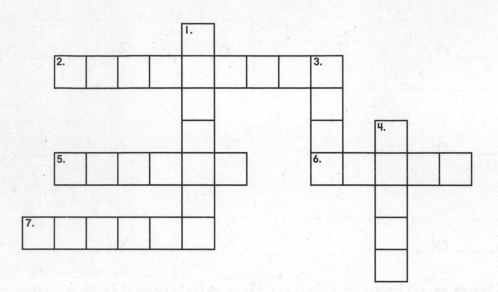

Across

2. friendly or inviting

5. a round shape

6. to break or destroy

7. in a direction of

Down

1. to fall over

3. to have gotten bigger

4. to go away from

 At Home: Help your child create a puzzle that uses the following words: *welcoming, grew, toward,* and *wreck.*

© Macmillan/McGraw-Hill

As you read <u>Sand Castle</u>, fill in the Cause and Effect Chart.

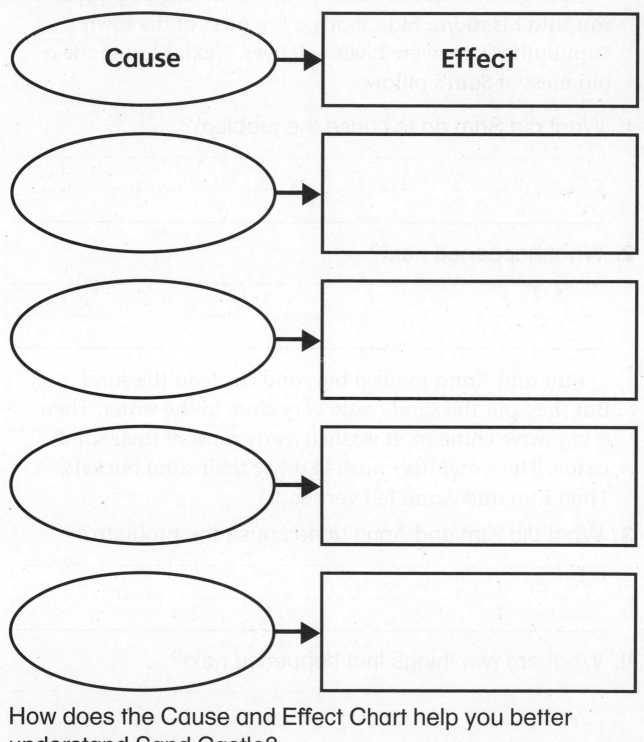

Cause → Effect

How does the Cause and Effect Chart help you better understand <u>Sand Castle</u>?

 At Home: Have your child use the chart to retell the story.

Sand Castle • Book 1.5/Unit 6 **259**

Read the story. Then answer the questions.

Sam did not shut the door to his room. His dog, Max, ran into his room. Max made a big mess of the town Sam built. There were blocks all over. Next, Max made a big mess of Sam's pillow.

1. What did Sam do to cause the problem?

_____

- -

_____

2. What happened next?

_____

- -

_____

Kim and Anna made a big sand castle in the sand. But they put the sand castle very close to the water. Then a big wave came in. It washed away most of their sand castle. The water also washed away their sand buckets. Then Kim and Anna felt very sad.

3. What did Kim and Anna do to cause the problem?

_____

- -

_____

4. What are two things that happened next?

_____

- -

_____

 At Home: Have your child draw two pictures showing a cause and effect sequence. Then ask your child to make up a story to describe the picture sequence.

As I read, I will pay attention to vocabulary words.

	"What are dioramas?" asked Sam.
5	"They are models of places," said Ms. Carlson. "I'll show
15	you one."
17	Ms. Carlson took out a small box. Inside was a model of
29	a farm. There was a plastic red barn. There were cows and
41	horses made of clay. There was paper grass that made a
52	meadow.
53	"We can go to the library," said Ms. Carlson. "You can
64	look at books to help you choose your habitats.
73	Later, everyone was whispering about their ideas. Nina
81	decided to make a desert habitat.
87	"I'll put sand in my diorama," said Nina. "I'll make
97	lizards and snakes. I'll try to make cactus plants." 106

Comprehension Check

1. What are dioramas?

2. What other animals could be in the farm diorama?

	Words Read	–	Number of Errors	=	Words Correct Score
First Read		–		=	
Second Read		–		=	

At Home: Help your child read the passage, paying attention to the goal at the top of the page.

Name _____

Read the sentence. Use context clues to figure out the meaning of the <u>underlined</u> word. Write the correct meaning on the line.

greeting	people who protect or keep watch
very big	broke into small pieces

1. My Nana visited a real castle with an <u>enormous</u> moat

   _____

   -

   going all the way around it. _____

2. The drawbridge almost <u>crushed</u> a small boat that was in

   -

   its way. _____

3. In the old days, kings had <u>guards</u> at the gate to protect

   _____

   -

   the castle from enemies. _____

4. Today, there are guides at the
   gate <u>welcoming</u> visitors.

   _____

   - - - - - - - - - - - - - -

At Home: Ask your child to write a three-sentence story about a castle. Encourage the use of at least two of the underlined words on this page in the story.

© Macmillan/McGraw-Hill

Name _____

Use the letters <u>oi</u> or <u>oy</u> to finish the words.

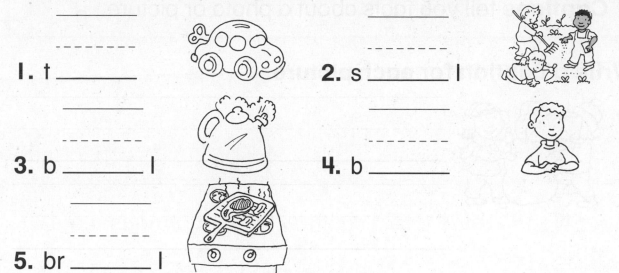

1. t _____

2. s _____ l

3. b _____ l

4. b _____

5. br _____ l

Now use the words in sentences.

6. _____

7. _____

8. _____

9. _____

10. _____

© Macmillan/McGraw-Hill

At Home: Have your child identify other words with the diphthong /oi/ spelled *oi* and *oy*. Ask your child to use some of the words in sentences.

Name _____

Captions tell you facts about a photo or picture.

Write a caption for each picture.

1.

_____

_____

_____

2.

_____

_____

_____

3.

_____

_____

_____

4.

_____

_____

_____

At Home: Have your child draw a picture and write a caption for it.

Name _____

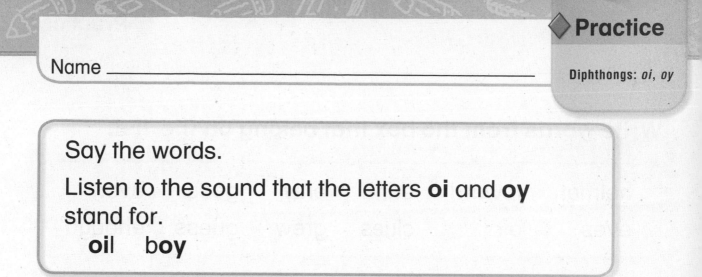

Say the words.

Listen to the sound that the letters **oi** and **oy** stand for.

oil   b**oy**

Complete each word by writing the letters <u>oi</u> or <u>oy</u>.

1. c_____n

2. s_____l

3. t_____

4. b_____l

Write a short story. Use as many <u>oy</u> and <u>oi</u> words as you can.

_____

_____

_____

_____

At Home: Have your child write another word that has the same vowel sound as *oil*. Then ask for a word with the same vowel sound as *boy*.

Write words from the box that belong on the list.

helmet	toward	earth	only	goes	ever
eyes	air	clues	grew	guess	enough

Things You Can Touch

_____   _____

- - - - - - - - - - - - - - -   - - - - - - - - - - - - - - - -

_____   _____

_____   _____

- - - - - - - - - - - - - - -   - - - - - - - - - - - - - - - -

_____   _____

Circle the word that completes each sentence.

1. The birds flew _____ the pond.
    across   been

2. The _____ bear was sleeping in the cave.
    gone   wild

3. The cub was _____ around in the water.
    fooling   other

© Macmillan/McGraw-Hill

Name _____

**Read each question. Look at the picture. Circle
<u>yes</u> or <u>no</u>. Then write each answer in a sentence.**

1. Is air invisible?

yes   no

2. Is a train wreck good?

yes   no

3. Has he been searching for food?

yes   no

4. Do you learn at school?

yes   no

5. Do you laugh enough on an
ordinary day?

yes   no

© Macmillan/McGraw-Hill